Welcome

Responsible for two of the three legs that comprise United States Nuclear Triad, the Air Force Global Strike Command (AFGSC) manages the country's fleet of strategic bombers and Intercontinental ballistic missiles (ICBM) and related support aircraft and systems. The long-range bombers first proved their strategic value during World War Two and, along with the ICBM force, have been a major component in the nation's defence planning for more than eight decades. Although AFGSC is the youngest of the air force's major commands, its role as the largest combat arm of the US Strategic Command (USSTRATCOM) is arguably the most important in deterring a nuclear conflict. The command has a rich history that is linked to the Strategic Air Command and can further be traced to the establishing of the Continental Air Forces on December 15, 1944.

Today, the command, which is headquartered at Barksdale Air Force in the Shreveport-Bossier City area of northwestern Louisiana, develops and provides combat-ready forces for nuclear deterrence and global strike operations in support of conventional warfare operations. It is responsible for the nation's three intercontinental ballistic missile wings, the USAF's entire bomber force, which includes active-duty and reserve component B-52H, B-1B and B-2A wings, the Long Range Strike Bomber programme, Air Force Nuclear Command, Control and Communications (NC3) systems and operational and maintenance support to organisations within the nuclear enterprise.

This special publication breaks down the aircraft, weapons and organisations that support the USSTRATCOM and America's other combatant commands.

Tom Kaminski
Editor

16

Contents

6 **"To Deter and Assure"**
The history, mission and organisation of the Air Force Global Strike Command.

14 **Base Map**
A guide to the key locations of AFGSC

16 **The Stratofortress**
The oldest operational aircraft on the USAF inventory continues to serve more than 70 years after the prototype's first flight.

24 **New power for the BUFF**
A long-awaited programme will provide AFGSC's long-range strike platform with new powerplants to extend its service life.

30 **Bad to the Bone**
Although no longer tasked with a nuclear mission, the B-1B Lancer remains an important asset in the USAF's ability to conduct long range strike missions.

40 **Spirit in the sky**
The USAF's only long-range penetrating bomber, the B-2A provides capabilities that are currently not matched by any other aircraft.

50 **Stealthy Raider**
The next-generation B-21A stealth bomber will become an important component of the USAF's planning in the near future.

58 **Arming the bombers**
The USAF's bomber fleet is capable of carrying a large inventory of conventional and nuclear weapons that is constantly being upgraded and modernised.

66 **America's doomsday aircraft**
The E-4B NAOC ensures America can respond to an attack or natural disaster in the event that conventional communication links are broken.

30

50

72 Mercury rising
Originally developed for the US Navy, the E-6B was updated to support USAF missions.

78 Silos in the heartland
The USAF's Intercontinental Ballistic Missile fleet is deployed in silos spread across five of the central United States.

88 Securing the silos
A small fleet of helicopters that provided rotary wing support to the USAF's intercontinental ballistic missile sites is being replaced.

96 Deploying the bombers
Although based in the United States, the USAF's bomber fleet is often deployed worldwide for exercises, combat or as a show of force.

104 Desert testers
Located in southern California's Mojave Desert, Edwards Air Force Base is home to the USAF's primary developmental flight test centre.

108 Humble, approachable and credible: the USAF Weapons School
Former Commander of the B-52 Weapons School Brian Rogers explains the history and mission of the USAF's postgraduate-level training organisation.

58

88

ISBN: 978 1 83632 043 2
Editor: Tom Kaminski
Senior editor, specials: Roger Mortimer
Email: roger.mortimer@keypublishing.com
Cover Design: Steve Donovan
Design: SJmagic DESIGN SERVICES, India
Advertising Sales Manager: Sam Clark
Email: sam.clark@keypublishing.com
Tel: 01780 755131
Advertising Production: Becky Antoniades
Email: Rebecca.antoniades@keypublishing.com

SUBSCRIPTION/MAIL ORDER
Key Publishing Ltd, PO Box 300, Stamford, Lincs, PE9 1NA
Tel: 01780 480404
Subscriptions email: subs@keypublishing.com
Mail Order email: orders@keypublishing.com
Website: www.keypublishing.com/shop

PUBLISHING
Group CEO and Publisher: Adrian Cox

Published by
Key Publishing Ltd, PO Box 100, Stamford, Lincs, PE9 1XQ
Tel: 01780 755131
Website: www.keypublishing.com

PRINTING
Precision Colour Printing Ltd, Haldane, Halesfield 1, Telford, Shropshire. TF7 4QQ

DISTRIBUTION
Seymour Distribution Ltd, 2 Poultry Avenue, London, EC1A 9PU
Enquiries Line: 02074 294000.

"To Deter and Assure"

One of nine major commands (MAJCOM) within the US Air Force, the Air Force Global Strike Command/Air Forces Strategic – Air (AFGSC/AFSTRAT-AIR) was provisionally established at Bolling Air Force Base (AFB), Washington DC, on January 12, 2009. Formally activated at Barksdale AFB in Louisiana on August 7, 2009, the command was created in the wake of several incidents involving the security of nuclear weapons and components that occurred in 2007 and 2008. At that time, it became clear that the strategic nuclear assets required additional oversight, so the decision was made to reunite the nuclear bomber and missile fleets and consolidate control under a single major command and a formal plan for the creation of AFGSC was announced in October 2008.

Responsibility for the USAF bombers, tankers and intercontinental ballistic missile fleets had been assigned to the Strategic Air Command (SAC) since it was established on March 21, 1946. Shortly after the 1991 collapse of the Soviet Union, the US Air Force initiated a major reorganisation that resulted in the deactivation of the Strategic (SAC), Tactical (TAC) and Military Airlift Air Commands (MAC) and created the Air Combat Command (ACC) and Air Mobility Command (AMC) on June 1, 1992.

As part of this reorganisation, SAC's Intercontinental Ballistic Missile (ICBM) and strategic bomber fleets and most of TAC's tactical strike aircraft were aligned under the newly activated ACC. Most of the tanker aircraft that supported SAC's bomber fleets were transferred to AMC, but a number were also aligned under ACC, the Pacific Air Forces (PACAF) and US Air Forces Europe (USAFE). In a subsequent change, the ICBMs and their support helicopter fleet were transferred to the Air Force Space Command (AFSPC) on July 1, 1993.

The AFGSC assumed control of the ICBM force from AFSPC on December 1, 2009, and on February 1, 2010, the long-range, nuclear-capable B-2A and B-52H bomber fleets were realigned from ACC to the new command.

Headquartered at Barksdale AFB in Bossier City, Louisiana, and led by a four-star General Officer, the MAJCOM is the warfighting air component of the United States Strategic Command (USSTRATCOM). As a global warfighting combatant command (CCMD), USSTRATCOM is responsible for strategic deterrence, nuclear operations, nuclear command, control and communications (NC3) enterprise operations, joint electromagnetic spectrum (EMS) operations (JEMSO), global strike and missile threat assessment.

Serving as USSTRATCOM's warfighting Component MAJCOMs (C-MAJCOM), the AFGSC and AFSPC are tasked to execute deterrence, assurance and global strike missions.

The Nuclear Triad

The US maintains a nuclear force that credibly deters adversaries, assures allies and partners, achieves the nation's objectives should deterrence fail and hedges against uncertain threats. Since the 1960s, these objectives have been met by the US Nuclear Triad, comprised of sea-based, land-based and airborne forces that provide the backbone for America's national security. Each leg of the Triad provides unique and complementary capabilities intended to dissuade an attack by an adversary. According to former Chairman of the Joint Chiefs of Staff General Mark A Miley: "The Nuclear Triad has kept the peace since nuclear weapons were introduced and sustained the test of time. The Triad and assigned forces provide deterrence, preventing catastrophic actions from the nation's adversaries. These forces stand ready to deliver a decisive response, anywhere, anytime, if required."

The Nuclear Triad currently includes:

• 240 Trident D5 submarine-launched ballistic missiles (SLBMs) deployed aboard 14 Ohio-class fleet ballistic missile submarines (SSBNs), known as 'boomers'. A portion of the SSBN fleet is always on patrol, making it difficult for potential adversaries to keep track of all of them. Each 'boomer' is capable of carrying up to 20 SLBMs.

E-4B 73-1676 lifts off from Offutt AFB, Nebraska, on August 24, 2024. The National Air Operations Center platform is operated by the 595th Command and Control Group's 1st Airborne Command and Control Squadron and reports to the Air Force Global Strike Command. USAF

A B-2A departs from Naval Support Facility Diego Garcia for an Operation Iraqi Freedom bombing mission while other aircraft from 40th Air Expeditionary Wing prepare to launch on March 20, 2003. At the time the bombers were assigned to Air Combat Command. USAF/SrA Nathan G. Bevier

• 400 land-based LGM-30G Minuteman III intercontinental ballistic missiles (ICBMs) deployed in hundreds of hardened silos spread across five states. ICBMs can be launched and reach targets within minutes, creating a nearly insurmountable targeting problem for adversaries. The missiles are the most responsive leg of the Triad and are maintained on alert on a 24-hour, 7-day basis.

• 60 nuclear-capable B-52H and B-2A heavy bombers. Capable of delivering gravity bombs and cruise missiles, the manned bombers provide a clear and visible signal of US intent and resolve during a crisis. Manned bombers provide a variety of deployment and yield options when placed on alert.

The strategic forces are supported by a secure nuclear command, control and communication (NC3) network.

As recently as March 1, 2023, the US had 1,419 nuclear warheads deployed on 662 missiles and bombers.

The Command

Tasked to develop and provide combat-ready forces for nuclear deterrence and global strike operations, AFGSC is responsible for the nation's 450 LGM-30 Minuteman III ICBMs and the operational fleet of B-2A, B-52H and B-1B strategic bombers. AFGSC assumed responsibility for the conventional mission assigned B-1Bs and 7,000 personnel previously assigned to ACC on October 1, 2015. The command's assets and nearly 34,000 personnel are assigned to two numbered air forces (NAF). ▶

Operating over the Pacific Ocean, a B-1B from the 9th Expeditionary Bomb Squadron was deployed from Dyess AFB, Texas, to Andersen AFB, Guam, on July 30, 2017. USAF/A1C Christopher Quail

A 54th Helicopter Squadron UH-1N flies over a missile alert facility near Minot AFB, North Dakota, on July 26, 2018. The squadron supports the 91st Missile Wing by providing rapid transportation for 91st Security Forces Group defenders. USAF/SrA Jonathan McElderry

The command's dual-capable bomber fleet is the most visible leg of the Nuclear Triad that includes ICBMs and SLBMs. Although the former SAC's bombers stood down from the 24/7 nuclear alert mission in September 1991, the capability to deliver the weapons has been retained. However, as a result of arms limitation treaties, the number of vehicles that are capable of delivering the weapons has been drastically reduced.

In accordance with the 2010 New Strategic Arms Reduction Treaty (New START), by 2018 the USAF fleet of nuclear-capable strategic bombers was reduced to just 66 aircraft. At that time the fleet was comprised of 46 B-52Hs and 20 B-2As that were dual-capable (nuclear and conventional) and 30 B-52Hs and 63 B-1Bs that were limited to conventional capability.

Organisation

Headquartered at Barksdale AFB, Louisiana, the Eighth Air Force/Air Forces Strategic (8AF/AFSTRAT) is assigned responsibility for AFGSC's manned bombers, which are assigned to five active-duty bomb wings (BW). A single Air National Guard wing and an Air Force Reserve Command (AFRC) wing and group share the responsibility for operating the B-2A, B-52H and B-1B bombers at Barksdale AFB, Whiteman AFB in Missouri and Dyess AFB in Texas. Co-located with the AFGSC at Barksdale and led by a two-star major general, 8AF serves as the Component Numbered Air Force (C-NAF) for USSTRATCOM. Serving as the air-based component of the nuclear triad, the bomber force is the most flexible and visible leg.

According to recent testimony from the commander of the USSTRATCOM: "The US bomber force represents an incredibly versatile set of tools." The bomber and tanker fleets support both nuclear and conventional operations, enabling the execution of strike options to support national objectives worldwide. The bomber fleet's dynamic force employment versatility makes it an indispensable Triad component."

The command's bombers provide conventional support for US Northern Command (NORTHCOM), US Central Command (CENTCOM), US European Command (EUCOM), US Pacific Command (PACOM) and US Southern Command (SOUTHCOM) as required and are regularly deployed in support of expeditionary operations. The command exercises annually

A pair of B-52Hs representing the 5th Bomb Wing's 69th Bomb Squadron and the 49th Test and Evaluation Squadron are prepared for a mission at Minot AFB, North Dakota, on July 7, 2022. The units executed combined sorties allowing for close collaboration and validation of tactics, techniques, and procedures developed through integrated flight test. USAF/A1C Alexander Nottingham

Equipped with a mixed load of 500lb and 2,000lb joint direct attack munitions, a B-52H receives fuel from a 340th Expeditionary Air Refueling Squadron KC-135R during a flight in support of Operation Inherent Resolve on June 9, 2017. USAF/S Sgt. Michael Battles

same day. The aircraft are a component of the nuclear command, control, and communications (NC3) network and serve as part of the aerial layer of the command-and-control node. On September 4, 2024, the USAF announced plans to provisionally activate the 95th Wing at Offutt AFB on October 1, 2024. Once established, the wing will assume control over the 595th CACG and the NAOC and NC3 missions.

Located at Offutt AFB, the 625th Strategic Operations Squadron (STOS) was originally activated on April 15, 1996, as a component of the US Space Command known as the 625th Missile Operations Flight (MOF). It assumed its current designation on June 14, 2007, and was realigned under the AFGSC on December 1, 2009. It has been assigned to the 595th CACG at Offutt since October 1, 2016.

The squadron's Airborne Launch Control System (ALCS) Combat Operations Flight provides airborne missileers for the USSTRATCOM's Airborne Command Post ▶

with every combatant command and joint partners through the Bomber Assurance and Deterrence (BAAD) mission.

An example of that mission occurred on July 1, 2015, when two B-52s conducted a 44-hour nonstop mission from Barksdale AFB to Australia's Northern Territory and delivered inert conventional bombs against targets on the Delamere Air Weapons Range. The BAAD mission was carried out as part of the Pentagon's effort to reassure allies in Asia amid heightened tensions due to China's construction of military facilities on disputed islands in the South China Sea.

In addition to the bomber fleets, the 8AF is responsible for the 595th Command and Control Group (CACG) and its 1st Airborne Command and Control Squadron (ACCS) and the 625th Strategic Operations Squadron (STOS). The group is a tenant activity at ACC's Offutt AFB in Nebraska, operating the E-4B National Airborne Operations Center (NAOC) aircraft. The 595th CACG was activated on October 1, 2016, and assumed responsibility for the 1st ACCS from ACC's 55th Wing the

Three B-1Bs from the 7th Bomb Wing at Dyess AFB, Texas, led by 86-0098, share the ramp at Tinker AFB, Oklahoma, on January 17, 2019. The bombers were receiving upgrades at Tinker's MRO Training Center. USAF/Greg L. Davis)

B-2A 88-0329 and 93-1085 are prepared for a mission at Andersen AFB, Guam, on April 6, 2005. The Spirit of Missouri *and* Spirit of Oklahoma *are operated by the 509th Bomb Wing. USAF*

(ABNCP) aboard the US Navy's E-6B aircraft. As integral members of the battle staff, the ALCS crew provides a survivable means to launch the nation's ICBM force. Additionally, the personnel provide intelligence, ad-hoc targeting, missile warning, battle damage assessment and ballistic missile defence support for the Airborne Emergency Actions Officer (AEAO) aboard the Mercury. The ICBM Targeting Flight maintains current and accurate targeting for the Minuteman fleet. Additionally, assigned personnel produce targeting and range safety

analysis for all ICBM test launches and support AFGSC software tests.

The 8AF commander is also responsible for the Joint – Global Strike Operations Center (J-GSOC). Established at Barksdale AFB in May 2018, the J-GSOC is the warfighting air component of USSTRATCOM and consists of the 608th Air Operations Center (AOC), the Joint Nuclear Operations Center (JNOC) and the Standoff Munitions Application Center (SMAC).

The 608th AOC plans, directs, monitors and assesses long-range strike missions in support of USSTRATCOM and theatre geographic combatant commands. Located at Barksdale, the 608th AOC also executes USSTRATCOM's air tasking cycle and provides the Joint Force Air Component Commander (JFACC) with assessments of operational-level plans for

all bomber sorties. Additionally, it serves as the COMAFSTRAT – Air/JFACC commander's primary command and control node and provides situational awareness of all USSTRATCOM airborne and alert aircraft.

Activated at Barksdale AFB in October 2018, the JNOC manages strategic bomber, reconnaissance and ICBM capabilities that are provided to USSTRATCOM. The centre's Bomber and Reconnaissance Divisions are responsible for planning, co-ordinating, tasking, monitoring and assessing nuclear-capable bombers and strategic weapons and nuclear-capable reconnaissance aircraft. The divisions co-ordinate with USSTRATCOM, ACC, AFGSC, J-GSOC and subordinate organisations, to synchronise daily aircraft utilisation in support of combatant commander objectives. Additionally, it reports aircraft and sensor status/locations to enhance nuclear and conventional operations in support AFSTRAT-Air/JFACC and USSTRATCOM.

The ICBM Division is tasked with monitoring and reporting of all missile field operations and activities. It observes, tracks and reports operational nuclear combat capability at AFGSC's Launch Control Centers and its launch facilities. The division also provides the AFSTRAT-Air/JFACC and the J-GSOC situational awareness

B-2A 88-0329 from the 509th Bomb Wing conducts a training flight near Whiteman AFB, Missouri, on July 28, 2005. The wing's combat-coded B-2As are operated by the 393rd Bomb Squadron.
Don Logan via Tom Kaminski

Two B-52Hs from the 2nd Bomb Wing are escorted by Japanese Air Self Defence Force F-15Js during a continuous bomber presence mission over the Pacific on July 26, 2018. USAF/MSgt. E. Taylor Worley

and expertise regarding missile field major maintenance activities, nuclear weapons convoy movements, security status and Nuclear Command, Control, Communications (NC3) status. JNOC's ICBM subject matter experts serve as a primary interface between operations at the missile wings and the USSTRATCOM Global Operations Center on behalf of the AFSTRAT-Air/JFACC and the J-GSOC.

Realigned under the J-SOC in August 2018, the SMAC is a Total Force organisation that includes military, government and contractor personnel. The centre was used operationally for the first time in a combat tasking on August 24, 2018, when two B-1Bs operating from Al Udeid Air Base in Qatar launched 19 AGM-158B joint air-to-surface stand-off missiles (JASSM-ER) against chemical weapons targets near Damascus, Syria.

AFGSC's Twentieth Air Force (20AF) controls three missile wings (MW) that are responsible for approximately 450 LGM-30 Minuteman III ICBMs including 400 that are operationally deployed. Led by a major general and headquartered at FE Warren AFB, Wyoming, the command's missiles are located in a series of underground silos that spread out along the northern tier of the Midwest US. Additionally, since March 27, 2015, the 20AF has been responsible for the 582nd Helicopter Group, which assumed responsibility for three helicopter squadrons that had previously been assigned directly to the individual missile wings. ▶

A pair of B-52Hs assigned to the 23rd Expeditionary Bomb Squadron taxi for take-off at Andersen AFB, Guam, at the start of a routine Bomber Task Force mission, while an Iowa Air National Guard KC-135 waits its turn on February 14, 2024. USAF/MSgt. Amy Picard

Two B-52H Stratofortresses conduct a routine training mission over the Pacific Ocean on August 2, 2018. This mission was flown in support of US Indo-Pacific Command's continuous bomber presence operations. USAF/A1C Gerald R. Willis

testing associated with the USAF's new B-21A bomber is assigned to the 412th TW's 420th FLTS at Edwards.

Stationed at Dyess, Whiteman and Barksdale, the 77th, 325th and 340th Weapons Squadrons are GSUs of ACC's 57th Wing and the USAF Weapons School (USAFWS) at Nellis AFB, Nevada. Each provides advanced training in weapons and tactics employment to senior aircrews, utilising aircraft assigned to the host wings.

The responsibility for lifecycle management of the bomber fleet is assigned to the USAF Sustainment Center's Oklahoma City Air Logistics Complex (OC-ALC) at Tinker AFB, Oklahoma. B-2A programmed depot maintenance (PDM) and major modifications are typically carried by Northrop Grumman at its Aircraft Integration Center of Excellence in Palmdale, California. Work on the B-52Hs and B-1Bs is generally carried out by OC-ALC's 76th Aircraft Maintenance Group (AMXG) at Tinker. ■

Testing, tactics and maintenance

Development testing of the command's operational bombers is the responsibility of Air Force Materiel Command's Air Force Test Center (AFTC) at Edwards AFB, California, and is conducted by the 412th Test Wing's (TW) 419th Flight Test Squadron (FLTS). The 'Global Bombers' test squadron operates examples of each of AFGSC's bombers. Also located at Edwards, the 31st Test & Evaluation Squadron (TES) is tasked with conducting combined operational and developmental testing utilising the bombers assigned to the 419th FLTS. It is a geographically separate unit (GSU) of the 53rd Wing's 753rd Test & Evaluation Group (TEG), which is a component of ACC's USAF Warfare Center at Nellis AFB, Nevada. Based respectively at Barksdale, Whiteman, Dyess and Edwards, the 49th, 72nd, 337th and 417th Test & Evaluation Squadrons are also GSUs of the 53rd TEG and conduct operational test and evaluation using aircraft assigned to the host wings. Developmental

A pair of B-1Bs support a North American Aerospace Defense Command (NORAD) exercise by entering Air Defense Identification Zone (ADIZ) off the east coast of North America during Operation Noble Defender on June 26, 2023. US Air National Guard/MSgt. Bryan Hoover

T-38A 65-10324 returns to Whiteman AFB, Missouri, at the conclusion of a mission on October 5, 2004. The 509th Bomb Wing's 13th Bomb Squadron operates 14 Talons in the companion trainer role. Don Logan via Tom Kaminski

Wing/Group	Squadron	Location	Aircraft	Tail Code
CHIEF OF STAFF, US AIR FORCE – Washington, D.C.				
Air Combat Command (ACC) – Joint Base Langley-Eustis, Virginia				
USAF Warfare Center (USAFWC) – Nellis AFB, Nevada				
53rd Wing		**Eglin AFB, Florida**		
753rd TEG		**Eglin AFB, Florida**		
	31st TES (Note 1)	Edwards AFB, California	B-1B, B-2A, B-52H	ED
	49th TES	Barksdale AFB, Louisiana	B-52H	OT
	72nd TES (Note 1)	Whiteman AFB, Missouri	B-2A	WM
	337th TES	Dyess AFB, Texas	B-1B	OT
	417th TES (Note 1)	Edwards AFB, California	B-21A	ED
57th Wing		**Nellis AFB, Nevada**		
USAFWS		**Nellis AFB, Nevada**		
	77th WPS	Dyess AFB, Texas	B-1B	WA
	325th WPS (Note 1)	Whiteman AFB, Missouri	B-2A	WM
	340th WPS (Note 1)	Barksdale AFB, Louisiana	B-52H	LA
Air Force Global Strike Command (AFGSC) – Barksdale AFB, Louisiana				
Eighth Air Force/Air Forces Strategic (8AF/AFSTRAT) – Barksdale AFB, Louisiana				
595th CACG	1st ACCS	**Offutt AFB, Nebraska**	E-4B	
	625th STOS	Offutt AFB, Nebraska	(No aircraft assigned)	
2d BW/OG	11th BS (FTU) (Note 2)	**Barksdale AFB, Louisiana**	B-52H	LA
	20th BS	Barksdale AFB, Louisiana	B-52H	
	96th BS	Barksdale AFB, Louisiana	B-52H	
5th BW/OG	23rd BS	**Minot AFB, North Dakota**	B-52H	MT
	69th BS	Minot AFB, North Dakota	B-52H	
7th BW/OG	9th BS	**Dyess AFB, Texas**	B-1B	DY
	28th BS (FTU)	Dyess AFB, Texas	B-1B	
28th BW/OG	34th BS	**Ellsworth AFB, South Dakota**	B-1B	EL
	37th BS	Ellsworth AFB, South Dakota	B-1B	
509th BW/OG	13th BS (FTU)	**Whiteman AFB, Missouri**	B-2A, T-38A	WM
	393rd BS	Whiteman AFB, Missouri	B-2A	
Air National Guard (ANG) Units – Joint Base Andrews-NAF Washington, Maryland				
131st BW/OG	110th BS (Note 3)	**Whiteman AFB, Missouri**	B-2A	WM
Tenth Air Force (10AF) – NAS JRB Fort Worth/Carswell Field, Texas				
Air Force Reserve Command (AFRC) Units - Robins AFB, Georgia				
307th BW/OG	93rd BS (FTU)	**Barksdale AFB, Louisiana**	B-52H	BD
343rd BS	(Note 4)	**Barksdale AFB, Louisiana**	B-52H	LA
489th BG	345th BS (Note 5)	**Dyess AFB, Texas**	B-1B	DY
Twentieth Air Force (20AF) – F.E. Warren AFB, Wyoming				
377th ABW		Kirtland AFB, New Mexico		
377th TEG	576th FLTS	Vandenberg SFB, California	(No aircraft assigned)	
582nd HG	37th HS	**F.E. Warren AFB, Wyoming**	UH-1N	FE
	40th HS	Malmstrom AFB, Montana	UH-1N	MM
	54th HS	Minot AFB, North Dakota	UH-1N	MT
	550th HS	Malmstrom AFB, Montana	MH-139A	MM
90th MW/OG	319th MS	**F.E. Warren AFB, Wyoming**	LGM-30G	
	320th MS	F.E. Warren AFB, Wyoming	LGM-30G	
	321st MS	F.E. Warren AFB, Wyoming	LGM-30G	
91st MW/OG	740th MS	**Minot AFB, North Dakota**	LGM-30G	
	741st MS	Minot AFB, North Dakota	LGM-30G	
	742nd MS	Minot AFB, North Dakota	LGM-30G	
341st MW/OG	10th MS	**Malmstrom AFB, Montana**	LGM-30G	
	12th MS	Malmstrom AFB, Montana	LGM-30G	
	490th MS	Malmstrom AFB, Montana	LGM-30G	
Air Force Materiel Command (AFMC) – Wright-Patterson AFB, Ohio				
Air Force Test Center (AFTC) – Edwards AFB, California				
412th TW/OG	419th FLTS	**Edwards AFB, California**	B-52H, B-1B, B-2A,	ED
	420th FLTS	Edwards AFB, California	B-21A	
USAF Sustainment Center (AFSC) – Tinker AFB, Oklahoma				
Oklahoma City Air Logistics Complex (OC-ALC) – Tinker AFB, Oklahoma				
76th AMXG	565th AMXS	Tinker AFB, Oklahoma	B-52H	
	567th AMXS	Tinker AFB, Oklahoma	B-1B	
Ogden Air Logistics Complex (OO-ALC) – Hill AFB, Utah				
309th MMXG	583rd MMXS	Hill AFB, Utah	(LGM-30G)	
Twenty-Second Air Force (22AF) – Dobbins ARB, Georgia				
Air Force Reserve Command (AFRC) Units – Robins AFB, Georgia				
413th FLTG		**Robins AFB, Georgia**		
	10th FLTS (Note 6)	Tinker AFB, Oklahoma	(B-1B, B-52H)	

Abbreviations

ABW	Air Base Wing
ACC	Air Combat Command
ACCS	Airborne Command & Control Squadron
AFB	Air Force Base
AFDW	Air Force District of Washington
AFGSC	Air Force Global Strike Command
AFMC	Air Force Materiel Command
AFRC	Air Force Reserve Command
AFTC	Air Force Test Center
AMXG	Aircraft Maintenance Group
AMXS	Aircraft Maintenance Squadron
ANG	Air National Guard
BG	Bomb Group
BS	Bomb Squadron
BW	Bomb Wing
CACG	Command and Control Group
FLTG	Flight Test Group
FLTS	Flight Test Squadron
(FTU)	Formal Training Unit
HG	Helicopter Group
HS	Helicopter Squadron
JB	Joint Base
JRB	Joint Reserve Base
MMXG	Missile Maintenance Group
MMXS	Missile Maintenance Squadron
MS	Missile Squadron
MW	Missile Wing
NAF	Naval Air Facility
NAS	Naval Air Station
OG	Operations Group
SFB	Space Force Base
STOS	Strategic Operations Squadron
TEG	Test & Evaluation Group
TES	Test & Evaluation Squadron
TW	Test Wing
USAF	United States Air Force
USAFWC	USAF Weapons Center
USAFWS	USAF Weapons School
USSF	US Space Force
WPS	Weapons Squadron

Air Force Global Strike Command Insignia

US Strategic Command Insignia

Notes

1. Utilises aircraft borrowed from its host wing.
2. Associate squadron operates alongside the 93d BS in the FTU role.
3. Wing operates B-2A as an associate to the 509th BW.
4. Squadron operates B-52H as an associate to the 2nd BW.
5. Wing operates B-1B as an associate to the 28th BW.
6. Flight test crews assigned to conduct functional check flights of modified and overhauled aircraft.

US AIR FORCE GLOBAL STRIKE

PACIFIC
OCEAN

**UNITED STATES AIR FORCE
GLOBAL STRIKE COMMAND
ASSOCIATED BASES**

COMMAND ASSOCIATED BASES

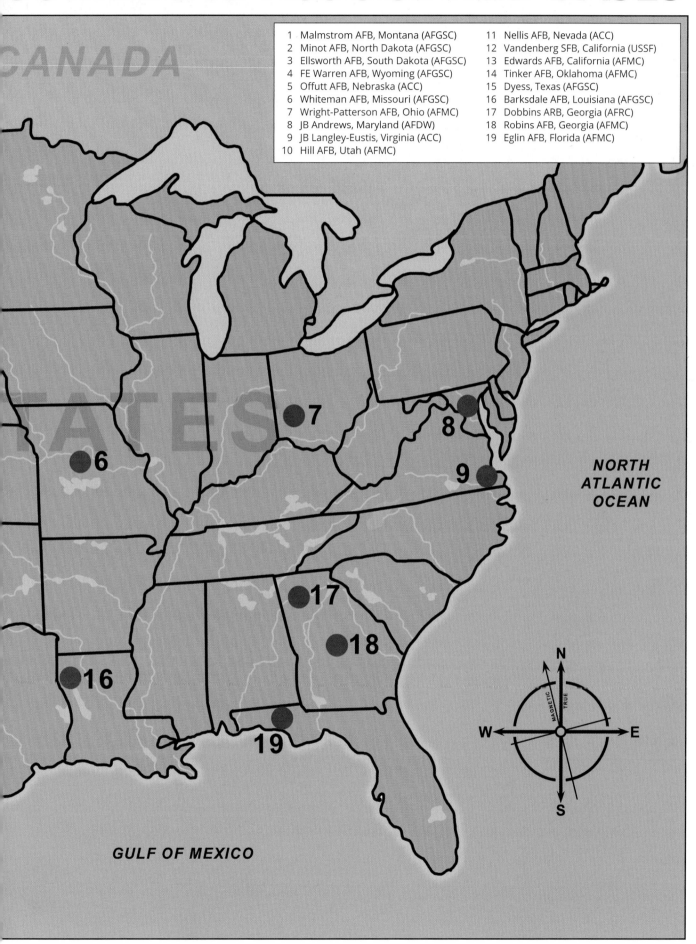

1 Malmstrom AFB, Montana (AFGSC)
2 Minot AFB, North Dakota (AFGSC)
3 Ellsworth AFB, South Dakota (AFGSC)
4 FE Warren AFB, Wyoming (AFGSC)
5 Offutt AFB, Nebraska (ACC)
6 Whiteman AFB, Missouri (AFGSC)
7 Wright-Patterson AFB, Ohio (AFMC)
8 JB Andrews, Maryland (AFDW)
9 JB Langley-Eustis, Virginia (ACC)
10 Hill AFB, Utah (AFMC)
11 Nellis AFB, Nevada (ACC)
12 Vandenberg SFB, California (USSF)
13 Edwards AFB, California (AFMC)
14 Tinker AFB, Oklahoma (AFMC)
15 Dyess, Texas (AFGSC)
16 Barksdale AFB, Louisiana (AFGSC)
17 Dobbins ARB, Georgia (AFRC)
18 Robins AFB, Georgia (AFMC)
19 Eglin AFB, Florida (AFMC)

The Stratofortress

Now the longest serving aerial weapon system in the US arsenal, the Boeing B-52 first flew in prototype form in Seattle, Washington, on April 15, 1952. It entered operational service with the USAF's Strategic Air Command (SAC) when the initial B-52B was delivered to 93rd Bombardment Wing, Heavy (93rd BMW) at Castle Air Force Base (AFB), California, on June 25, 1955. Boeing conducted the maiden flight of the first of 102 B-52H models on March 6, 1961, when serial 60-0006 lifted off from Wichita, Kansas. The variant entered operational service with the 379th Bombardment Wing, Heavy (BMW) at Wurtsmith AFB, Michigan on May 9, 1961. Production of the bomber included 744 aircraft in nine versions and the last B-52H was delivered on October 26, 1962.

Since entering the inventory, the bomber has been continually upgraded with new equipment and weapons, allowing it to be adapted for missions that have evolved to meet changing requirements. The venerable long-range heavy bomber has an impressive combat history that includes the Vietnam conflict and Operations Desert Storm, Desert Fox, Desert Strike, Allied Force, Enduring Freedom, Iraqi Freedom, Inherent Resolve and Resolute Support.

Originally designed to penetrate Soviet air defences and deliver nuclear weapons, the Stratofortress design included a conventional role that was first demonstrated operationally on June 18, 1965, when 27 B-52Fs struck enemy targets in South Vietnam. Subsequently the Stratofortress flew missions in support of the

war in Southeast Asia until August 15, 1973, when B-52Ds and B-52Gs flew the final sorties over Cambodia. Throughout that period, the bombers flew 126,615 missions from bases in Guam and Thailand. During that period 18 bombers were lost to enemy fire and 13 were written-off due to other operational causes.

The aircraft flew its first strikes over Iraq in support of Operation Desert Storm in January 1991. When the conflict ended, it had conducted about 1,620 sorties and delivered more than 26,000 tonnes of ordnance, accounting for 40% of the weapons dropped by coalition forces.

Since then, the bombers have supported operations around the globe, conducting missions over Iraq, Afghanistan, and Syria. From

wings and several test and training units. Four combat-coded active-duty USAF squadrons are responsible for 48 bombers and 18 are assigned to the AFRC, in support of training requirements. Operational commitments are also supported by an AFRC associate squadron, while an active associate squadron supports training requirements. Four grounded B-52Hs are utilised as maintenance trainers. One GB-52H is assigned to each bomb wing, while the second pair support Air Education & Training Command's 82nd Training Wing at Sheppard AFB, Texas. Ten airframes are stored with the 309th Aerospace Maintenance & Regeneration Group (AMARG) at Davis-Monthan AFB, Arizona. Ten B-52Hs have been lost to crashes, the most recent during an aborted take-off at Anderson AFB, Guam, on May 18, 2016.

The fleet's 44 combat-coded bombers are divided between the 2nd Bomb Wing (BW) at Barksdale AFB, Louisiana, and the 5th BW at Minot AFB, North Dakota. Each of the operational active-duty squadrons is assigned 11 combat-coded aircraft and one that is designated as Back-up Aircraft Inventory (BAI).

Since 2009, the AFRC's 307th BW at Barksdale has been designated the Stratofortress Formal Training Unit (FTU). The wing's 18 B-52s include 16 that are coded for training and two BAI airframes. The transfer of the 'schoolhouse' mission to the AFRC was announced by the Air Force Chief of Staff General Norton A Schwartz on March 9, 2009. Activated at Barksdale and assigned to the AFGSC on January 1, 2011, the 307th is responsible for the 93rd BS. Previously a combat-coded squadron, it assumed the role from the 2nd BW's 11th BS, which now operates as an associate squadron alongside the AFRC unit. Its aircrews and maintenance personnel support the 'schoolhouse' operations, under the direction of the reserve squadron. The first students graduated from the 93rd's 32-week training course in October 2009.

Activated at Barksdale on April 1, 2010, and assigned to the 307th BW, the 343rd BS operates as a classic associate unit and provides crews that operate combat-coded bombers under the direction of the 2nd BW.

A B-52H assigned to the 49th Test & Evaluation Squadron (TES) at Barksdale is coded for operational test and evaluation (OT&E), along with a BAI airframe. The squadron is a geographically separated unit (GSU) under ACC's 53rd Wing at Eglin AFB, Florida. Support for the bomber is provided by the AFRC's 307th BW. A second pair of bombers support ▶

B-52H 60-0001 from the 2nd Bomb Wing at Barksdale AFB, Louisiana, operates alongside a Royal Netherlands Air Force F-16A with its weapons bay open during an April 2015 joint training mission over Europe. *USAF*

April 2016 to April 2018, B-52Hs, operating from Al Udeid Air Base, Qatar, flew combat 1,850 sorties against ISIS and Taliban forces. The bomber's most recent combat missions took place in 2021, when six aircraft from the 23rd Expeditionary Bomb Squadron flew 240 combat missions during the US withdrawal from Afghanistan.

As a result of the break-up of the Soviet Union, the B-52 fleet stood down from nuclear alert on September 27, 1991. The aircraft has served as the backbone of the manned strategic bomber force and has been tasked with various missions, including strategic attack, close air support, air interdiction, offensive counter-air, and maritime global strikes. Despite a career that has spanned nearly 64 years, the B-52

remains an important asset and is expected to continue in service through 2040.

Operations

On June 1, 1992, SAC's bomber fleet, which was then assigned to nine wings, was realigned under the newly created Air Combat Command (ACC). At the time the fleet included both B-52G and B-52H models. However, in May 1994, the last B-52Gs were retired and, by the end of that year, the operational B-52H fleet was consolidated at just two bases. In a subsequent change, the Air Force Global Strike Command (AFGSC) assumed control of the long-range, nuclear-capable B-2A and B-52H bomber fleets on February 1, 2010. The inventory currently includes 76 aircraft assigned to the three bomb development test and evaluation (DT&E) at Edwards AFB, California. Both are operated by the 412th Test Wing's 419th Flight Test Squadron (FLTS). The wing is a component of the Air Force Materiel Command's Air Force Test Center at Edwards.

Originally known as the Weapons School B-52 Division, the 340th Weapons Squadron (WPS) is a GSU assigned to the 57th Wing's USAF Weapons School at Nellis AFB, Nevada, which is an ACC-assigned organisation. Located at Barksdale, the squadron's graduate-level instructor courses provide B-52H crews with advanced training in weapons and tactics employment utilising bombers assigned to the 307th BW.

Upgrades

The USAF continues to modernise the aircraft, and the latest series of upgrades will allow the venerable bomber to remain in service until 2050 or beyond. Besides physical modifications, system upgrades are incorporated as part of the B-52 Software Block (BSB). The software changes allow

engineers to make the bomber compatible with new weapons or equipment.

First installed in 1980, the B-52's ASQ-176 Offensive Avionics System (OAS), which controls navigation and weapons delivery, received a significant upgrade that was completed in 2009. Replacing obsolete systems, the Avionics Midlife Improvement (AMI) modernised several of the bomber's systems that were rapidly approaching obsolescence, including the inertial navigation system, avionics control unit and data transfer system. New equipment comprised ring laser gyro inertial navigation units, upgraded processors and software, as well as mission planning hardware and associated software. Flight testing began in mid-December 2002 and was completed in early 2004. In addition to providing the aircraft with upgraded capabilities, the modifications served as a building block for the enhancements that have followed.

The Combat Network Communications Technology (CONECT) upgrade provided new multi-functional colour displays (MFCD), computer architecture, multiple data links and

5th Bomb Wing insignia

enhanced voice communications capabilities, plus an advanced wideband satellite terminal. The first operational B-52H to receive the upgrade arrived at Tinker AFB, Oklahoma, on July 16, 2013. Installed by the Oklahoma City Air Logistics Complex (OC-ALC) at a cost of $1.1 billion, it enabled network-centric operations (NCO) providing crews with the capability to receive and send real-time digital information, including intelligence, mapping, and targeting data, and to communicate with other platforms via satellite. Providing enhanced situational awareness for the crew, the upgrade significantly enhanced the bomber's ability to conduct close air support (CAS) missions. The integrated suite allowed mission re-tasking and weapons re-targeting for the now-retired AGM-86C/D CALCM and the AGM-158 joint air-to-surface stand-off missile/JASSM-extended range (JASSM/JASSM-ER) J-series weapons. In addition, a new digital interphone system designed to survive and function through the nuclear environment has been incorporated. Like the AMI, the CONECT was intended as the basis for future upgrades.

Boeing began development of the upgrade in March 2005 and modification of the first aircraft took place at Boeing's Wichita, Kansas, facility in October 2007. The first B-52H fitted with CONECT carried out its initial test flight there on May 21, 2009. It was formally turned over to the 412th Test Wing at Edwards AFB for developmental testing on August 5, 2009, and carried out its initial test flight there on January 17, 2010. Flight testing at Edwards AFB was completed in December 2011. Modifications to the first production aircraft began in July 2013 and were carried out by the 565th Aircraft Maintenance Squadron (AMXS) during the bomber's normal programmed depot maintenance (PDM) cycle at the Oklahoma City Air Logistics Complex (OC-ALC) at Tinker. Delivery of the first operational B-52H with CONECT to Barksdale AFB was on April 21, 2014. Two ground instructional training aircraft (GITA) also received the CONECT modifications.

Integration of the advanced extremely high frequency (AEHF) satellite communication system gave Stratofortress crews the ability to exchange information through family of advanced beyond line-of-sight terminals (FAB-T), which enable communication with ground, air, and space platforms. The nuclear command and control network and communication system (NC2NCS) integrated a secure, survivable two-way EHF SATCOM link

Operating over the Mediterranean on April 9, 2018, a Stratofortress from the 5th Bomb Wing breaks away after receiving fuel from a 100th Air Refueling Wing KC-135R. USAF/A1C Benjamin Cooper

B-52Hs from the 5th Bomb Wing's 23rd and 69th Bomb Squadrons share a rainy ramp at Minot AFB, North Dakota on November 2, 2018. Minot is the northernmost bomber base in the US. USAF

Three B-52Hs assigned to the 2nd Bomb Wing at Barksdale AFB, Louisiana fly in a formation after completing missions over the Baltic Sea during Bomber Task Force Europe 20-1, on October 23, 2019. USAF/SSgt Trevor T McBride

that permits transmission and acknowledgment of emergency action messages in accordance with Joint Chiefs of Staff (JCS) nuclear protected information exchange requirements (IER).

The USAF also upgraded the fleet with Mode S/5 identification friend or foe (IFF), which allows the aircraft to operate safely in controlled airspaces in the evolving air traffic environment. It was one of several communication navigation surveillance/air traffic management (CNS/ATM) capabilities developed for the B-52.

The B-52H's Northrop Grumman APQ-166 strategic radar was last upgraded in 1985, and the mechanically scanned array (MSA) radar has become increasingly unserviceable and is nearing the end of its useful life. The B-52 Radar Modernization Program (RMP) supports nuclear and conventional operations by upgrading or replacing the AN/APQ-166 radar. The programme will increase system reliability, reduce sustainment costs, and improve the capabilities of the aircraft to employ an array of weapons and perform mission-essential navigation and weather avoidance functions. The system adds improved mapping and detection range, an increase in the number of targets it can simultaneously engage and enhanced reliability due to updated systems and operating software. The system will also provide the bomber with new capabilities that include the ability to track moving surface and air targets.

The B-52H RMP entered the engineering and manufacturing development (EMD) phase when a five-year contract was awarded to Boeing on June 14, 2021. A critical design review was conducted in February 2022. As part of the EMD effort Boeing began modifying the first of two test aircraft after a B-52H from the 307th BW's 93rd BS arrived at its San Antonio, Texas, facility on May 25, 2023.

Developmental and integrated flight testing will begin in Fiscal Year (FY) 25, leading to initial operational test and evaluation (IOT&E), full rate production and operational fielding in mid-FY27. The Raytheon AN/APG-79 active electronically scanned array (AESA) system pairs the sensor from the F/A-18's AN/APG-79V4 with the processor from the F-15's AN/APG-82 and is assigned the designation AN/APQ-188. The project is expected to cost about $2.8 billion and achieve initial operational capability in 2027. Delivery of the first fully modified RMP test aircraft to Edwards AFB will permit the start of system-level open-air developmental testing.

A two-part Milestone C decision is planned in FY25 that will support the modification of 28 low rate initial production (LRIP) aircraft. A full rate production (FRP) decision for the remaining 46 aircraft will follow IOT&E in FY27. The RMP is scheduled to achieve initial operating capability in 2027. The upgrade will also affect all three weapon system trainers (WST), the WST Training Systems Integration Laboratory (SIL), both B-52 offensive station maintenance trainers (OSMT) and the bombing-navigation system maintenance trainers (BNSMT).

On June 6, 2024, L3Harris Technologies was awarded a $34 million contract to modernise the B-52H cockpit as part of the AFGSC's B-52 Quad Crew Program. Whereas the B-52H is currently operated by a five-person crew that includes two pilots, two navigators ➤

B-52H 60-0024 deploys a braking parachute after landing at RAF Fairford, United Kingdom, on November 4, 2019. US Navy/MC2 Eric Coffer

and an electronic warfare officer, the new programme will consolidate the functions of the electronic warfare officer and navigator into a single position.

The aircraft's operational effectiveness will be further enhanced by additional communications upgrades that are under development. Integration of the bomber tactical data link (TDL) with the B-52 will provide jam-resistant situational awareness and command/control via a line-of-sight (LOS) Link 16 capability. The programme will integrate a Link 16 terminal and multi-functional information distribution system joint tactical radio system (MIDS-JTRS) terminals. The TDL terminal and LOS capability will be integrated with the CONECT subsystem. Mandated by the National Security Agency (NSA) and Department of Defense, Crypto Modernization will upgrade the aircraft with a mobile user objective system (MUOS) capable radio to support secure beyond line of sight (BLOS) voice and data communications via the Second Generation Anti-Jam Technical UHF Radio for NATO (SATURN) network and upgraded SATCOM systems. The Very Low Frequency/Low Frequency (VLF/LF) Modernization programme will provide the B-52 with a secure, survivable receive-only VLF strategic communications system needed for strategic nuclear command and control.

A B-52H Stratofortress assigned to the 23rd Expeditionary Bomb Squadron, departs from Andersen AFB, Guam, on February 3, 2024.
USAF/MSgt Amy Picard

489th Bomb Group insignia

Targeting pods

The B-52H fleet was first equipped with electro-optical/infrared sensors in 1972, when the AN/ASQ-151 electro-optical viewing system (EVS) was first installed. Located under the nose section in steerable chin turrets, the system consists of the Raytheon AN/AAQ-6 forward-looking infrared (FLIR) in a starboard turret and Northrop Grumman AN/AVQ-22 low-light-level television camera (LLTV) in a port turret. Primarily used for low-level navigation, the images from the EVS were displayed on monochrome screens on the flight deck and the navigator station. Unlike newer electro-optical/infrared (EO/IR) systems, the EVS did not provide a targeting capability.

Led by the weapons school and test communities that developed tactics, techniques, and procedures in the 1990s, B-52s began employing laser-guided Paveway munitions. However, being unable to designate the targets meant 'buddy lase' tactics were used, where the B-52H would deliver the weapons against targets designated by another targeting pod-equipped aircraft such as an F-15E or F-16C. The success of this led the USAF to provide the bomber with an autonomous targeting pod capability. The first evaluation with the bomber was in 2003, when AN/AAQ-28 LITENING II pods were installed on two B-52Hs from the AFRC's 93rd BS at Barksdale AFB. Initial test flights took place in March 2003. The pod was first used operationally during Operation Iraqi Freedom (OIF) to deliver laser-guided GBU-12 Paveway II munitions against targets in northern Iraq on April 11, 2003. The 93rd BS later achieved full combat ready status with the pod in July 2006.

The success of this programme led to the entire fleet receiving a precision strike capability. Integration of the AN/AAQ-33 Sniper advanced targeting pod (ATP) began in September 2008, when Boeing received a $15 million contract to integrate the system. Operated from the navigator's station, the ATP gave the B-52H the capability to acquire real-time intelligence, surveillance, and reconnaissance (ISR) with full-motion video, to provide overwatch presence and deliver

B-52H 60-0034 Wise Guy prepares to depart Tinker AFB, Oklahoma, on March 9, 2021. The Stratofortress was stored with the 309th Aerospace Maintenance and Regeneration Group at Davis-Monthan AFB, Arizona, from 2008 to 2019 before being regenerated to active service by the Oklahoma City Air Logistics Complex. USAF/Paul Shirk

A B-52H from the 5th Bomb Wing departs Minot AFB, North Dakota, while participating in Exercise Prairie Vigilance 24-3 on April 12, 2024. USAF/A1C Kyle Wilson

precision guided weapons in support of ground forces. In addition to giving aircrews a critical long-range, positive target identification capability, the system's video downlink permits ISR information to be transmitted to forward-deployed forces. In August 2009, the USAF awarded Lockheed Martin a contract to fully integrate the pod by linking pod control, display and target geo-location with the bomber's offensive avionics system (OAS) via the new multi-function colour display and digital-integrated hand controller. Today, the B-52H can carry either the LITENING or Sniper pod.

Expanding arsenal

The USAF has continually developed the bomber's systems to ensure it remains capable of delivering both nuclear and conventional weapons. Although the Stratofortress is no longer considered capable of flying into heavily defended airspace, its ability to loiter for long periods makes it the ideal platform to drop long-range precision guided conventional weapons. Additionally, it remains capable of delivering stand-off nuclear weapons, making it a vital part of the US nuclear deterrent. Under the terms of the current New Strategic Arms Reduction Treaty (START), the US is permitted a maximum of 60 nuclear capable bombers, comprising 16 B-2As and 44 B-52Hs. As a result, the USAF removed the nuclear weapons capabilities from 30 of its 76 operational B-52s in 2015.

With a weapons payload of more than 70,000lb, the B-52H is already capable of carrying the most diverse range of weapons of any combat aircraft in the USAF inventory. For the nuclear mission, the B-52H can be equipped with up to 20 AGM-86B air-launched cruise missiles (ALCMs), comprising six under each wing on SUU-67/A pylons and eight in the bomb bay on the Common Strategic Rotary Launcher (CSRL).

While the CSRL is also capable of carrying up to eight B61-7 or B83-1 nuclear gravity bombs, in 2020, the AFGSC confirmed that the weapons had been removed from the weapon's inventory. As a result, the bomber's nuclear capabilities were limited to the AGM-86B and the future AGM-181 long-range stand-off (LRSO) weapon. The stealthy long-range weapon will ensure the B-52 can carry out strikes deep in enemy territory from stand-off ranges.

For conventional missions, the B-52H can employ a very wide range of munitions using both internal and external carriage options. Underwing conventional 'stub' pylons, equipped ▶

AF 60 034

Wearing markings to honour the bomber's Arc Light missions in Southeast Asia, B-52H 61-0005 from the 69th Expeditionary Bomb Squadron taxies at RAF Fairford, UK, on May 24, 2024. The bomber was deployed in support of a Bomber Task Force Europe mission. USAF/SSgt Emily Farnsworth

Iraqi Freedom. JDAM achieved limited initial operational capability in 1998 and the B-52H was the first aircraft to be equipped with the JASSM, which was cleared for operational use in October 2003.

The steady shift away from ballistic 'dumb' ordnance and toward employment of precision weapons led to integration of the MIL-STD-1760 databus capability to the internal weapons bay. Carried out under the Advanced Weapons Integration (AWI) programme and the 1760 internal weapons bay upgrade, the effort expanded the aircraft's conventional weapons carriage capability by modifying equipment and software. The USAF designated 40 CSRLs as being excess to nuclear requirements and dedicated them to strictly conventional missions. As part of the project, the CSRLs were modified to carry a new integrated weapons interface unit (IWIU). Previously tested on a CSRL in 2005, the IWIU was already incorporated on the aircraft's external wing pylons and provides for the carriage and delivery of smart weapons. In the June 2005 test, a B-52H equipped with

with the Heavy Stores Adapter Beam (HSAB) can carry up to nine weapons, each weighing more than 3,000lb. An alternative external weapons carriage option involves modified AGM-28 Hound Dog missile pylons. Each pylon is equipped with two multiple ejector racks that enable the bomber to carry 12 weapons under each wing.

The HSAB pylons support the widest range of conventional ordnance available. With two pylons, the B-52H can carry 16 wind-corrected munitions dispensers (WCMD), 12 AGM-154 joint stand-off weapons (JSOW), 12 AGM-158 joint air-to-surface stand-off missiles (JASSM) or 12 joint direct attack munitions (JDAM).

For weapons such as the 500lb- class Mk82 low drag general purpose (LDGP) bomb and similarly sized naval mines, the bomb bay is fitted with three cluster racks. Each rack has nine stations, enabling the carriage of up to 27 weapons in the bay. For 2,000lb-class weapons, two four-station clip-in racks are used. Weapons in that class include the Mk84 GP bomb and Mk60 and Mk65 naval mines.

Whereas the WCMD was first deployed over Afghanistan in 2002, the JSOW entered service in 2003 and was deployed during Operation

A B-52H from the 5th Bomb Wing conducts aerial refuelling with a KC-135R assigned to the 350th Expeditionary Air Refueling Squadron, during a mission over the US Central Command area of responsibility on June 12, 2024. USAF/MSgt Matthew Plew

Assigned to the 20th Expeditionary Bomb Squadron, B-52H 60-0024 takes off from Mihail Kogălniceanu Air Base, Romania, during Bomber Task Force Deployment 24-4, on July 27, 2024. USAF/SrA Seth Watson

a prototype of the Boeing IWIU released eight 2,000lb joint direct attack munitions (JDAM) from the aircraft's internal bomb bay at the Utah Test and Training Range. Once equipped with the IWIU, the launchers were no longer capable of deploying nuclear weapons and were referred to as common rotary launchers (CRL). The aircraft's stores management and offensive avionics software were also incrementally updated to enable the carriage and employment of eight 2,000lb GBU-31, 500lb GBU-38 JDAM and GBU-54 laser JDAM, AGM-158 JASSM and JASSM-Extended Range (JASSM-ER), ADM-160B miniature air-launched decoy (MALD) and ADM-160C MALD-jammer (MALD-J). Subsequent updates provided the capability to carry the family of WCMDs, laser guided bombs (LGB) and additional weapons such as the 2,000lb GBU-56 laser JDAM, as well as mixed loads on the CRL. According to Lt Gen James Kowalski, former commander of Air Force Global Strike Command: "The B-52 delivers the widest variety of stand-off, direct-attack nuclear and conventional weapons in the USAF." The capability boosts the number of weapons the B-52H can carry from 12 to 20, providing an increase of 60%.

Elected officials have recently recommended that the USAF shore up the country's nuclear capabilities by restoring the ability to deliver those weapons on 30 B-52Hs that were limited to carrying conventional weapons under the New START treaty, which will expire in February 2026. Language inserted into the 2025 Defence Bill by the House and Senate Armed Services Committees would require the USAF to begin modifying the bombers within a month of the treaty's expiration and be completed by 2029.

The move is a response to Russia's suspension of the treaty and China's rapidly expanding strategic warhead production. The New START treaty limited both US and Russia to 1,550 deployed warheads. Although the two governments agreed to extend the treaty for five years in 2021, Russia suspended its participation in 2023 amid heightened tensions with NATO over its invasion of Ukraine. The USAF has estimated the cost to restore capability will be about $4.5 million.

A B-52H from the 96th Expeditionary Squadron prepares to refuel from a KC-135 over the Pacific on February 24, 2022. USAF/SSgt Lawrence Sena

Support

Boeing has provided engineering support for the B-52 since delivery of the first examples nearly 60 years ago. In April 2019, it received a USAF contract to provide continued engineering support for the B-52H fleet. As part of the B-1/B-52 Flexible Acquisition and Sustainment contract, which could be worth as much as $14 billion, Boeing is supporting both bomber fleets with hardware and software development and integration, ground and flight testing, configuration management, studies and analyses, modernisation and other tasks as directed by the USAF over a period of 10 years.

Structurally, the fleet is considered to be in good shape and has significant service life left. The Oklahoma City Air Logistics Center's B-52 Sustainment Division (GKD) is responsible for the total lifecycle management of the fleet, including efforts associated with development, modification, test, sustainment, and support. The 76th Maintenance Wing's 76th Aircraft Maintenance Group is responsible for carrying out programmed depot maintenance (PDM), repairs and modifications for the B-52H fleet. Its 565th Aircraft Maintenance Squadron (AMXS)

conducts PDM on around 17 B-52Hs annually, with each aircraft being rotated through the depot every four years. Air Force Materiel Command monitors and tracks the bombers by tail number and the service provided during PDM is virtually tailor-made for each individual airframe based on numerous factors, including its flight profiles. During PDM, the aircraft often receive minor modifications to improve the integrity of the structures, reduce corrosion and enhance safety. This includes minor service life extension efforts, replacing obsolete or removing inactivated systems and carrying out weight reduction initiatives. These efforts will soon encompass replacing the bombers' eight Pratt & Whitney TF33 turbofan engines with more modern Rolls Royce powerplants under the Commercial Engine Replacement Program (CERP).

Continued modernisation efforts will ensure that the B-52H's systems remain as capable as the airframe. The upgraded bombers could serve the USAF until 2060, meaning the B-52H could conceivably still be in service when Boeing and USAF celebrate the centenary of the YB-52's maiden flight. ∎

B-52H 60-0036 receives fuel from a KC-10A from the 22nd Air Mobility Wing at Travis AFB over Southern California on May 16, 2024. USAF/Todd Schannuth

New power

The B-52H first flew in Wichita, Kansas on July 20, 1960, but unlike the earlier versions of the bomber that were powered by eight General Electric J57 turbojet engines, it was equipped with Pratt & Whitney TF33-P-3 (JT3D) turbofans. In addition to being cleaner burning and quieter than the turbojets, the turbofans delivered almost 25% more thrust and reduced fuel consumption by 15%.

Studies and proposals

Replacing the TF33s was considered as early as 1971, when Boeing first looked at re-engining the B-52G/H fleets under Project Seek Four. In 1982, Pratt & Whitney proposed replacing the TF33s with the same F117-PW-100 (PW2000) engines that power the Boeing C-17A airlifter. Between 1995 and 2015, government agencies and contractors carried out no less than 13 studies/reviews that considered more capable and efficient powerplants. They looked at several different engine options and configurations under both direct purchase and various leasing arrangements.

A 1995 study prepared by the USAF's Oklahoma City Air Logistics Center, in response to a government requirement, determined the TF33s were the largest cost driver in B-52H operations. The study determined that providing the bomber with new engines would improve reliability and maintainability by 800%, while fuel efficiency would increase range by 30-40%. In response, the B-52 System Program Office identified options for installing four 40,000lb commercial engines.

In 1996, Boeing and its partners, which included Rolls-Royce, Allison and American Airlines, proposed replacing each of the eight TF33s on 94 B-52Hs with four Rolls-Royce RB211-535E4-B high bypass turbofans at a cost of $4.5 billion. The unsolicited proposal included new engine struts and cowlings, an auxiliary power unit and engine controls. Cockpit modifications provided three new flat panel displays for engine control and monitoring, along with new throttles and engine controls that were common with Boeing's 757 airliner. Additionally, an automatic rudder/autothrottle capability would enhance engine-out capability and new generators would provide additional power. The engines would be provided under a lease arrangement and supported through contractor maintenance.

Compared to the TF33s that delivered 17,000lb-st, the RB211 produced 43,100lb-st for take-off. The installation would have increased

A B-52H from the 5th Bomb Wing departs Nellis AFB, Nevada, during Red Flag-Nellis 22-1 on February 9, 2022. Whereas early versions of the B-52 were powered by eight Pratt & Whitney J57 turbojets, the B-52H received TF33 turbofans but retained the same eight engine configuration. USAF/William R Lewis

for the BUFF

total take-off thrust from 136,000lb-st to 172,400lb-st (766.87kN). According to Boeing, the conversion would have saved the USAF $4-6 billion over the 30-year lease. Largely due to the costs involved, the USAF rejected the proposal following a review by an integrated product team in 1997.

In March 2002, the USAF determined that the TF33 engines would power the B-52H for its remaining operational life, at the time expected to extend beyond 2045. The bomber's service life is limited by its upper wing surfaces, which have an estimated service life of 32,500-37,500 flight hours. Air Combat Command's Directorate of Requirements reported: "The TF33 engines currently installed on the B-52H are more than capable of meeting any current or future mission requirements and, as such, the air force has no plans to replace these engines." At that time, Pratt & Whitney had assured the air

force that the engines were fully supportable through 2040.

However, just three months later, the Under Secretary of Defense for Acquisition, Technology and Logistics (AT&L) commissioned the Defense Science Board (DSB) to review the need for replacing the TF33s. In a report released in March 2003, the DSB urged the USAF to re-engine the B-52H fleet "without delay". It determined that replacing the eight-engine configuration with four commercial high-bypass engines would provide greater operational flexibility. In addition to increasing range by about 46%, new engines would significantly reduce fuel consumption and in-flight refuelling and maintenance requirements. The DSB analysis concluded that the economic and operational benefits far outweighed the cost of the project. It estimated that re-engining 76 B-52Hs in "a fast-paced, low-risk acquisition track" from 2006-2011, would cost $3-3.5 billion. Additionally, the project could save the USAF $9-12 billion through 2037. Candidate engines were identified as the Rolls-Royce RB211, Pratt

& Whitney PW2040 and General Electric CF6-50 and CF6-80C2. Over the decade that followed, little more was mentioned on the topic and the bomber carried out its missions with the existing engines.

Renewed interest from the Air Force Global Strike Command (AFGSC) in 2014 resulted in yet another look at replacing the TF33s. In October, the Air Force Life Cycle Management Center's Propulsion Sustainment Branch released the first of two requests for information (RFI) specifying requirements for alternative engines.

By 2017, the Air Force Propulsion Directorate reported that the TF33 was not sustainable beyond 2030. A subsequent 2018 USAF briefing reported that the engines were "inefficient" and provided "limited capability relative to modern commercially available engines." Additionally, the TF33s were "costly and manpower-intensive to maintain." In August 2018, the Directorate revealed that overhaul costs had more than doubled over the past decade, largely due to parts obsolescence and a shrinking supplier base. With plans to retain the bombers in service until 2050 or beyond, the need to replace the TF33 had become a more pressing issue. ➢

Airmen replace one of the B-52H's eight TF33 turbofan engines at Andersen AFB, Guam, on April 25, 2021. USAF/SrA Jovante Johnson

One-for-one swap

After numerous failed attempts, the USAF finally began moving closer to providing the bombers with new engines under its Commercial Engine Replacement Program (CERP). Unlike earlier proposals, the CERP specified an eight-engine configuration utilising new commercial regional/business jet size turbofan. The CERP was intended to allow the Air Force Global Strike Command (AFGSC) "to fully utilise the capabilities of the B-52H aircraft to employ an array of nuclear and conventional weapons while saving fuel and extending the range/loiter capabilities of the aircraft."

Although consideration was given to a four-engine configuration, the cost to strengthen the wings and modifications to the internal systems and associated testing resulted in the USAF's decision to retain the dual-engine pod configuration. Replacing each twin-engine pod with one larger engine required flight testing to resolve engine-out asymmetric thrust recovery issues and that would reduce power by 25% rather than 12.5% in an eight-engine configuration. Engineering concerns also involved cockpit and control interfaces and the need for a quick start capability required by the nuclear Single Integrated Operational Plan (SIOP). Additionally, changes to the aerodynamics would require full weapons separation testing to be conducted.

The technology provided by the newer engines would improve reliability and maintainability of the propulsion system and provide additional electrical power generation capabilities to support future requirements.

Key requirements

- A baseline improvement in fuel consumption of 20%, with a goal of 40%
- Maintaining current performance capabilities, including take-off/combat ceiling performance and structural service life
- Minimising aerodynamic changes and modifications to the airframe and aircraft systems

Airmen from the 2nd Maintenance Squadron perform a periodic inspection on B-52H 61-0012 at Barksdale AFB, Louisiana, on November 24, 2014. USAF/A1C Mozer O Da Cunha

- Supporting a maximum take-off weight of 488,000lb
- Maintaining the bomber's centre of gravity, weapons carriage configuration and capacity and release envelopes
- A minimum 15–25-year utilisation before the first required engine overhaul, equivalent to a 6,000-hour service life before removal, with an 8,000-hour objective
- A viable 40-year maintenance concept
- Interchangeable quick engine change (QEC) kits and cowlings
- Full authority digital engine controls (FADEC)
- Quick engine start capability
- Engine monitoring system to record engine control/performance parameters, maintenance, and engine health data

Contract award

The service first received funding for the CERP under the Fiscal Year (FY) 2018 National Defense Authorization Act (NDAA), with around $10 million provided to study replacement of the TF33. An engine integration RFI was issued in February 2017, but Boeing was named as the sole source integrator for the CERP following a March 2018 material development decision. As part of its request for $280 million to upgrade the B-52H fleet, in FY 2019 the USAF included ➤

A pilot assigned to the 96th Bomb Squadron inspects the TF33 engine of a B-52H in preparation for a flight during Bomber Task Force Europe 20-1. USAF/A1C Duncan C Bevan

$64.5 million to conduct technical maturation and risk reduction (TMRD) efforts. A risk reduction requirement contract was issued to Boeing in December 2018.

The CERP's three-phase acquisition approach included pre-engineering manufacturing development (EMD), EMD and production and deployment. Pre-EMD efforts included a two-step engine source selection. During a technology maturation and risk reduction (TMRR) phase, the USAF identified qualified engine manufacturers that would work with Boeing to develop their integration approach. Following source selection, Boeing began design and integration efforts for virtual and physical prototype installations.

A request for proposals (RFP) for new engines that was released on May 19, 2020, called for engines that were military-specific derivatives of existing commercial engines. Respondents to the RFP included GE Aviation, Pratt & Whitney, and Rolls-Royce, which all offered FADEC-controlled, dual rotor/spool, axial-flow turbofans.

GE Aviation's proposals included the CF34-10 series and more advanced Passport 20 series turbofans. Where the CF34-10 powers the Embraer ERJ-190-100/200 regional airliner, the Passport 20 equips the Bombardier Global 7500/8000 business jets. Meanwhile, Pratt & Whitney offered a variant of the Pratt & Whitney Canada PW815GA, which received FAA certification in February 2017 and powered the Gulfstream Aerospace Gulfstream 600 business jet.

Under pre-EMD efforts, Boeing, which was the overall integrator for the re-engining and upgrades, and the USAF selected a variant of

the Rolls-Royce BR725 to replace the TF33s. The $2.6 billion B-52 CERP engine contract was awarded to Rolls-Royce in September 2021 and a preliminary design review was conducted in October 2022. Previously known as the BR700-725, the BR725 already powered the Gulfstream G650 business jet. Based on the BR700 series which was developed jointly by the BMW Rolls-Royce AeroEngines GmbH joint venture, the BR710 variant was already in service with the USAF under the designation F130, powering both the Bombardier/Northrop Grumman E-11A (Global 5000) and Gulfstream Aerospace C-37A (Gulfstream V). Normally produced in Germany by Rolls-Royce Deutschland Ltd, the BR725 would be assembled at the former Allison facility in Indianapolis, Indiana, allowing Rolls-Royce to meet the requirements for US content. The BR725 consists of a single-stage fan driven by a three-stage low pressure turbine, an annular combustion chamber, a ten-stage high pressure compressor driven by two-stage high pressure turbine to deliver a maximum of 16,900lb-st of thrust.

The B-52H CERP was initiated as a middle tier acquisition (MTA) rapid prototyping development programme that would conclude at the end of the rapid virtual system prototype (VSP) phase in FY 2023. Boeing delivered an initial VSP digital design in September 2021. In March 2022, the Air Force Acquisition Executive approved the programme's transition to a major capability acquisition (MCA) pathway. The MTA phase concluded in December 2023.

Initial testing of the F130-RR-200 side-by-side engines in a newly designed nacelle was carried out in three phases at the National Aeronautics and Space Administration's (NASA)

Rolls-Royce developed the rapid twin pod configuration for the B-52. Testing was initially tested on a special test rig at the NASA Stennis Space Center in Mississippi. Rolls-Royce

Each of the B-52H's eight TF33 turbofans will be replaced with modern Rolls-Royce F130 engines, after which the Stratofortress will be redesignated the B-52J. USAF

Stennis Space Center in Mississippi, beginning in early-2023. The combination was installed on a specialised test stand that permitted a complete two-engine pod to be operated under a variety of conditions. A giant wind fan tested the engines and rapid twin pod configuration in simulated crosswinds of up to 50kt from various directions, and another component in front of the engines simulated operations at various heights above a runway. Conducted at the Arnold Engineering Development Complex in Tullahoma, Tennessee, high-speed inlet verification wind tunnel testing was completed in June 2023.

Testing then shifted to the Rolls-Royce facility in Indianapolis, Indiana, in early August 2024, where sea-level testing of the first engine to test (FETT) evaluated the initial software release for the F130-RR-200 in a newly refurbished test cell.

A Milestone B decision that would allow the programme to enter the engineering and manufacturing development (EMD) phase was expected in FY 2024 but will likely slip into FY 2025. Completion of the system-level critical design review in 2025 will be followed by modification of two test aircraft under the EMD phase at Boeing's San Antonio, Texas,

facility beginning in 2026. Once modifications are completed, developmental and integrated flight testing will begin in 2028, leading to initial operational test and evaluation (IOT&E) in 2031.

Production modifications are now expected to be funded between 2028 and 2034, and the USAF currently estimates the cost of the programme will be $15 billion. The proposed programme will award low-rate initial production (LRIP) contracts to procure engines and modify 52 bombers prior to the completion of IOT&E. A full-rate production decision for the remaining 22 aircraft will follow in 2032. Production will be carried out at Tinker AFB, Oklahoma, where the Oklahoma City Air Logistics Complex carries out overhauls and modifications on 17 aircraft annually. Each of the bombers is rotated through the depot level maintenance facility at Tinker on a four-year rotation.

Integration

In addition to the new engines, airframe modifications will require upgraded nacelles and cowlings and redesigned struts incorporating new engine attachment fittings, a pre-cooler and revised electrical, hydraulic,

fuel and pneumatic interfaces with the existing aircraft systems. Modifications to the wing structure are understood to be limited to the incorporation of spar stiffeners. Because the number of generators will double to eight, electrical power generation capacity will be increased and require a modified power systems architecture. Additionally, wiring for full authority digital engine controls (FADEC) will be incorporated. Changes to the flight deck will include installation of digital engine controls and indicators, as well as new or modified throttle controls.

The CERP will also provide the B-52 with a Honeywell 36-150 auxiliary power unit (APU) that will enhance mission readiness and flexibility of aircraft operations. Serving as an auxiliary starter air unit (ASAU), it will permit the bomber to meet operational quick-starting requirements without the use of ground support equipment.

The CERP is the final phase of a multi-programme modernisation effort for the B-52H and follows the radar modernisation programme and multiple communication system upgrades. Upon completion of the CERP, the bomber will receive the designation B-52J. ∎

Bad to the Bone

The USAF describes the multi-mission B-1B Lancer as "the backbone of America's long-range conventional bomber force. [It] can rapidly deliver massive quantities of precision (and non-precision) weapons against any adversary, anywhere in the world, at any time."

The Lancer's operational career began nearly 40 years ago, and the bomber served as a workhorse for the USAF in the so-called War on Terror. Known affectionately as the 'Bone', the B-1B still holds records for speed, payload, range, and time of climb in its class. However, time and sustained combat operations have taken their toll on the bomber's airframe. Despite its age, recent structural issues, and the reduced size of the fleet, it remains one of the go-to platforms for the Air Force Global Strike Command (AFGSC) and will likely continue to serve well into the next decade or beyond.

Development and fielding

Originally developed by Rockwell International under the Advanced Manned Strategic Aircraft (AMSA) programme, the B-1A project was cancelled in June 1977 after four prototypes were built and tested. The programme was later resurrected and development of the B-1B began in October 1981.

Two B-1As initially supported the B-1B test programme. In October 1984, Rockwell carried out the first flight of the B-1B at its production site at Palmdale, California, adjacent to Air Force Plat 42, and delivered the first Lancer to the Strategic Air Command (SAC) 96th Bombardment Wing (BMW) at Dyess AFB on July 7, 1985.

The bomber achieved initial operational capability at Dyess on October 1, 1986, and Rockwell delivered the last of 100 B-1Bs to the 384th BMW at McConnell AFB, Kansas on May 2, 1988. Under SAC, Bones were operated by four wings, comprising the 28th, 96th, 319th and 384th BMWs and later by the Georgia and Kansas Air National Guard's 116th and 184th BMWs. A complete restructuring of the USAF saw the entire fleet realigned from SAC to the newly created Air Combat Command (ACC) on June 1, 1992. Subsequently the 319th and 384th Bomb Wings (BW) transferred their bombers to other units, including the 366th Wing at Mountain Home AFB, Idaho. In October 1993, the 96th BW at Dyess AFB, Texas, was redesignated as the 7th BW.

Activated at Barksdale AFB, Louisiana, on August 7, 2009, the AFGSC initially took control of the nuclear-capable B-52H and B-2A bombers, but assumed the responsibility for the entire manned bomber fleet on October 1, 2015, when the B-1Bs were transferred from ACC.

B-1Bs are currently assigned to AFGSC's 7th and 28th BWs at Dyess in Texas and Ellsworth AFB, South Dakota. They are flown by three combat-coded active-duty bomb

A B-1B departs Naval Support Activity Diego Garcia, British Indian Ocean Territory, for a strike mission against al Qaeda terrorist training camps and Taliban military installations in Afghanistan while supporting Operations Enduring Freedom on October 7, 2001. USAF

squadrons and another that is tasked as the formal training unit (FTU). Operations at Dyess are also supported by an Air Force Reserve Command (AFRC) associate squadron assigned to the 489th Bomb Group (BG). Additionally, the 53rd Wing at Eglin AFB, Florida, and the 57th Wing at Nellis AFB, Nevada, are responsible for geographically separated units (GSU) at Dyess. The 53rd's 337th Test & Evaluation Squadron (TES) 'Falcons' conducts operational test & evaluation, tactics development and evaluation for B-1B hardware, software, and weapons prior to fielding. Reporting to the USAF Weapons School as part of the 57th Wing, the 77th

Weapons Squadron (WPS) 'War Eagles' is tasked with providing the graduate-level weapons instructor course (WIC) to B-1B aircrew. At Edwards AFB, California, the 412th Test Wing's 419th Flight Test Squadron (FLTS) 'Silent Sting' carries out developmental testing of B-1B hardware, software, and weapons. Operational testing (OT) is also carried out at Edwards by the 53rd Wing's 31st TES 'Desert Pirates'.

Since entering service, 11 B-1Bs have been written-off in mishaps that occurred between September 1987 and January 2024. The original B-1B was retired August 8, 1988, and later scrapped. Since 2012, another retired bomber (85-0082) that had been stored at Davis-Monthan AFB, Arizona, has supported fatigue life evaluations being carried out by Boeing in Seattle, Washington. The contractor purchased Rockwell International's aerospace and defence businesses in December 1996.

In 2001, the decision was made to retire 33 B-1Bs, leading to the end of operations by the 366th Wing at Mountain Home AFB, Idaho, and the Air National Guard's 116th and 184th BWs at Robins AFB, Georgia and McConnell AFB, Kansas. Seven of those bombers were later returned to service.

Eight of the retired bombers were placed on static display at sites throughout the US, and 17 B-1Bs retired between 2002 and 2012 remain in storage with the 309th Aerospace Maintenance & Regeneration Group (AMARG)

7th Bomb Wing insignia

at Davis-Monthan AFB, Arizona. Another Lancer (85-0092) was removed from storage at Davis-Monthan and trucked to Kansas, where the Wichita State University's National Institute of Aviation Research (NIAR) is creating a 'digital twin' of the bomber. The digitised aircraft is supporting the creation of a tool that can predict where structural failures or damage may occur, to support the development of repairs, design modifications or revisions to structural inspection intervals, as well as re-evaluate the design life of the aircraft. ▶

Conventional missions

Although the long-range strategic bomber was designed to penetrate enemy defences at low altitude and high speed to deliver nuclear weapons, between November 2007 and March 2011 the Bone's nuclear capability was removed in accordance with the Strategic Arms Reduction Treaty (START). As a result, the Lancer fleet has since been limited to delivering conventional weapons.

Initiated in 1993, the Conventional Mission Upgrade Program (CMUP) modernised the B-1B's weapons capabilities. The CMUP initially optimised the bomber's ability to deliver 500lb Mk82 general-purpose bombs and added the capability to employ 1,000lb combined effects munitions. Additional weapons, including precision-guided munitions, were added through a series of blocks. The incorporation of a Mil-Std-1760 weapons bus and global positioning system (GPS) enabled the aircraft to deliver 2,000lb GBU-31 joint direct attack munitions (JDAMs). Subsequent block updates added the 500lb GBU-38 JDAM and GBU-54 Laser JDAMs, 250lb GBU-39 small diameter bomb (SDB I), wind corrected munition dispensers (WCMDs), AGM-154 joint stand-off weapons (JSOWs) and AGM-158A joint air-to-surface stand-off missiles (JASSMs) to the

bomber's payload, along with the ALE-50 towed decoy system.

The Lancer's versatility was further increased in 2008, when it gained the ability to carry an AN/AAQ-33 Sniper XR advanced targeting pod (ATP). Initially evaluated in response to a July 2006, Air Forces Central Command (AFCENT) urgent operational need request to install the ATP on the B-1B, testing of the Sniper was completed in February 2007. In addition to enabling positive target identification, the pod provides a remotely operated video enhancement receiver (ROVER) video downlink (VDL) capability, supporting laser guided weapons employment and expanding the bomber's non-traditional intelligence, surveillance, and reconnaissance (ISR) ability. It was first used in combat on August 4, 2008, when a 34th Expeditionary Bomb Squadron (EBS) B-1B successfully targeted enemy forces in Afghanistan with a GBU-38.

Improvements and upgrades

Beginning in 2012, the Reliability and Maintainability Improvement Program (RMIP) upgraded the B-1B's AN/APQ-164 radar. Besides serving as an all-weather area navigation aid, the radar provides a precise all-weather automatic terrain following (TF) and terrain

28th Bomb Wing insignia

avoidance (TA) capability, as well as a high-resolution synthetic aperture radar (SAR) for navigation and targeting.

Today, the long-range, multi-mission bomber carries the largest payload of guided and unguided conventional weapons in the USAF inventory and is capable of carrying a 75,000lb load for 7,455 miles. Stores are held in three weapons bays on a multi-purpose rotary launcher (MPRL) and enhanced conventional bomb modules (ECBM).

The B-1B was the first aircraft to field the Lockheed Martin AGM-158B JASSM-ER in 2015 and the AGM-158C long-range anti-ship missile (LRASM). It initially tested an LRASM against a maritime target on the Point Mugu Sea Range in August 2017. A subsequent test, conducted on December 8, 2017, saw the bomber launch two LRASMs that struck their intended targets. The LRASM achieved early operational capability (EOC) with the B-1B in December 2018.

Although the LASRM retains the JASSM-ER's imaging infrared (IIR) seeker, weapons datalink, and satellite-aided inertial navigation system, it also features a seeker that homes in on electromagnetic signals radiated by naval vessels and provides mid-course guidance. The missile provides the bomber with a flexible, long-range, advanced, anti-surface capability, with up to 24 LRASMs carried internally on the MPRL.

The B-1B was originally designed with the ability to carry and fire external weapons. However, in accordance with START, the

On of four 28th Bomb Wing assigned B-1Bs departs Ellsworth AFB, South Dakota, for a mission in support of Operation Odyssey Dawn over Libya, on March 27, 2011. USAF/SSgt Marc I. Lane

B-1B 85-0074 departs Tinker AFB, Oklahoma on its return flight to Dyess AFB, Texas after receiving the Integrated Battle Station modifications, on December 15, 2015, the largest modification programme in the bomber's history. USAF/Kelly White

B-1B's external hardpoints, which permitted the bomber to carry up to 14 AGM-86 cruise missiles, were rendered inoperative in 2011.

In December 2020, the USAF demonstrated the bomber's ability to deliver a JASSM carried on an external pylon. Reactivating the external stations would permit the bomber to carry 6-12 additional JASSMs or LRASMs externally or support the fielding of future hypersonic weapons, when they become available. Earlier in 2019, the USAF demonstrated additional B-1 carriage options that included the use of the external hardpoints and expanded internal bays capable of carrying large hypersonic cruise missiles.

The USAF now plans to reactivate this capability and increase the bomber's carriage capacity of stand-off munitions by integrating a newly developed external heavy-stores pylon. The B-1B had previously been tested with Boeing's load adaptable modular (LAM) pylon. Evaluations have included captive carry flights with the 2,000lb GBU-31 joint direct attack munition (JDAM), 5,000lb GBU-72 advanced bunker buster penetrating weapons and AGM-183 air-launched rapid response weapons (ARRW) that were completed in October and December 2023, respectively.

The 412th TW began formally testing the LAM pylon with one of the two B-1Bs operated by the 419th FLTS. The externally mounted pylon features relocatable modular attachment points that reduce the need for weapon-specific pylons and make it possible to test weapons for which an appropriate pylon may not exist. As a result, the B-1B is capable of testing larger hypersonic weapons. Each LAM has a capacity of up to 7,500lb. Mounting LAMs on all of the B-1B's external hardpoints would allow the bomber to carry 36 AGM-158 joint air-to-surface stand-off missiles (JASSM) or hypersonic attack cruise missiles (HACM), including 24 internally and 12 externally.

Combat operations and deployments

The B-1B was first used in combat during Operation Desert Fox on December 18, 1998. Operating from Sheikh Isa Air Base in Bahrain, four B-1Bs dropped 188 500lb Mk82 unguided bombs on Iraqi targets over a four-day period.

Beginning on April 1, 1999, six B-1Bs began flying combat missions in support of Operation

A 34th Expeditionary Bomb Squadron B-1B departs from Al Udeid Air Base, Qatar, on May 19, 2018, for a combat mission against the Taliban and other terrorist groups. USAF/SSgt Joshua Horton

A B-1B assigned to the 7th Bomb Wing at Dyess AFB, Texas, on an early morning training mission on February 21, 2021. USAF/A1C Josiah Brown

A deployed B-1B operated by the 34th Expeditionary Bomb Squadron, operates over the Pacific Ocean during a Bomber Task Force mission, on June 20, 2022. USAF/MSgt Nicholas Priest

Allied Force over Kosovo. Operating from RAF Fairford, UK, the bombers delivered more than 20% of the total ordnance but flew less than 2% of the combat sorties.

During the initial six months of Operation Enduring Freedom that commenced on October 7, 2001, eight B-1Bs dropped nearly 40% of the total tonnage delivered by coalition air forces. This included nearly 3,900 JDAMs, accounting for 67% of the total. Throughout Operation Iraqi Freedom, the bombers flew less than 1% of the combat missions but delivered 43% of the JDAMs used during the conflict.

The fleet was engaged in continuous combat operations from late-2001 through early-2016 and the 7th BW and 28th BW flew more than 14,000 combat missions in support of Operations Enduring Freedom, Iraqi Freedom and, more recently, Operations Odyssey Dawn, Freedom's Sentinel, and Inherent Resolve.

In January 2016, B-1Bs from Ellsworth AFB's 34th Expeditionary Bomb Squadron completed a six-month rotation to Al Udeid Air Base, Qatar, ▶

A pair of B-1Bs assigned to the 34th Expeditionary Bomb Squadron, over Royal Australian Air Force Base Darwin, Australia, before landing for fuel on June 22, 2022. USAF/TSgt Chris Hibben

marking the end of nearly 14 years of continuous bomber rotations in support of US Central Command (CENTCOM). Although temporary, the bomber's departure from the theatre was necessary to support fleet-wide upgrades.

B-1Bs returned to Southwest Asia in March 2018, when a pair of Lancers from the 28th BW's 34th EBS arrived at Al Udeid and conducted missions against ISIS targets in Syria in support of Operation Inherent Resolve. During those operations, two B-1Bs launched 19 JASSM missiles against chemical weapon facilities in Syria.

After conducting strikes against ISIS in Syria and Iraq, the B-1Bs were pulled from CENTCOM again in March 2019. During the final rotation, Lancers flew 390 sorties, totalling 4,471 hours, and conducted 920 air strikes. They returned in October, when four Lancers from Ellsworth arrived at Prince Sultan Air Base in Saudi Arabia in response to aggression from Iran. The short deployment concluded five days later when the bombers returned home.

The Lancers were the last USAF bombers deployed to Al Udeid, where they conducted combat operations against ISIS in Iraq and Syria as part of Operation Inherent Resolve. The bombers also conducted 'over the horizon' flights to strike the Taliban and other targets in Afghanistan.

More recently, on February 1, 2024, B-1Bs were launched from Dyess AFB and delivered more than 125 precision munitions at 85 targets across seven facilities in Iraq and Syria. The bomber's

first long duration CONUS-to-CONUS mission was carried out against Iran's Islamic Revolutionary Guards Corps (IRGC) Quds Force and Iranian-backed militia groups. The air strikes were carried out in retaliation for attacks facilitated by the IRGC against US and coalition forces in the region. Targets included command and control operations centres, intelligence centres, rocket, missile and unmanned aerial vehicle storage sites and logistics and munition supply chain facilities.

Improved systems

Initiated in 2012, the $1.25 billion Integrated Battle Station (IBS) and Sustainment Block 16

489th Bomb Group insignia

(SB-16) project was the largest modification ever implemented for the Lancer. It improved situational awareness and battlefield communications, reduced crew workload and added time-critical targeting and precision engagement capabilities.

Developed by Boeing, the IBS/SB-16 project combined three separate upgrades and equipped the Lancer with a fully integrated datalink (FIDL) that enabled line-of-sight (LOS) and beyond-line-of-sight (BLOS) command and control (C2) connectivity and supported time-critical targeting operations. It also updated the central integrated test system (CITS), which performs onboard diagnostics of the aircraft. That modification installed a new computer and large LCD display located between the defensive (DSO) and offensive system officer (OSO) crew stations in the aft cabin.

The Vertical Situation Display Upgrade (VSDU) replaced the pilot and co-pilot's primary flight displays and flight instruments with four new colour screens and six new multi-function displays at the DSO and OSO stations. Operation of the glass cockpit systems and sensors was enhanced by SB-16A software that updated navigation, weapon delivery, radar, diagnostics, electrical multiplexing, communication/navigation management and controls and displays systems.

The 7th Bomb Wing at Dyess received the first operational IBS-equipped B-1B, when serial 86-0122 touched down on January 21, 2014. The upgrade achieved initial operational capability

Another recent project replaced the B-1B's AN/APQ-164 radar with a new scalable agile beam radar global strike (SABR-GS) active electronically scanned array (AESA). The SABR-GS is based on the Northrop Grumman AN/APG-83 and provides the bomber with advanced operational capabilities including large synthetic aperture radar (SAR) maps, advanced image processing and sensor integration. Its open architecture provides the B-1B with new ISR and targeting capabilities and supports the integration of data from other current and planned sensors.

Operations

Operational B-1Bs are stationed at Dyess and Ellsworth AFBs and support testing at Edwards AFB. Operational missions at Dyess are assigned to the 9th BS 'Bats', while the 28th BS 'Grim Reapers' is tasked as the FTU. At Ellsworth, both the 34th BS 'Thunderbirds' and the 37th BS 'Tiger' are operational combat-coded units.

The activation of the 489th BG at Dyess on October 17, 2015, marked the first time that the AFRC had been involved in B-1B operations. Assigned to the 307th BW at Barksdale AFB as a GSU, the group's single squadron operates B-1Bs assigned to the 7th BW's 9th BS under a classic reserve association tasked with flying operational missions.

Lancers from the 28th Bomb Wing's 37th EBS first deployed to Andersen AFB, Guam, in support of the US Pacific Command's Continuous Bomber Presence (CBP) mission from September to December 2005. The unit was relieved by Bones from the wing's 34th EBS, which deployed to Andersen from December 2005 through April 2006. The responsibility for the mission was primarily shared between the B-52H and B-2A fleets until June 2010, when the mission was formally assigned to the USAF's four operational B-52H squadrons. B-1Bs returned to the CBP rotation on August 6, 2016, when Lancers assigned to the 34th EBS ▶

B-1B 85-0075 assigned to 34th Expeditionary Bomb Squadron, deploys flares during a Bomber Task Force mission over the Pacific Ocean, on June 25, 2022. USAF/MSgt Nicholas Priest

(IOC) in December 2015, following delivery of the 15th modified bomber. Upgrades were carried out during programmed depot maintenance at Tinker AFB's Oklahoma City Air Logistics Complex (OC-ALC). The programme concluded in September 2020, when serial 86-0133 returned to service at Dyess. Over an eight-year span, two prototypes and 60 production installations were carried out.

Communications upgrades provided the B-1B with a multifunctional information distribution system (MIDS) – joint tactical radio system (JTRS) and crypto-compliant radios that provide BLOS communications and meet National Security Agency and Department of Defense crypto-modernisation (CM) requirements. MIDS-JTRS also provides a multi-datalink capability that improves situational awareness and permits rapid inflight retargeting in co-operative combat environments.

The initial B-1B upgraded under the B-1 Embracing Agile Scheduling Team (BEAST) programme flew for the first time at Dyess AFB on September 8, 2023. BEAST updates the bomber's defensive avionics system and provides upgraded secure communications systems; a modernised identification friend-or-foe (IFF) system, a Link-16 tactical data communications capability and updated mass data storage. Normally, upgrades like BEAST are performed when the aircraft undergoes a scheduled depot maintenance cycle, but on this occasion are also being completed out of cycle to improve the aircraft's lethality more rapidly.

A pair of B-1Bs is intercepted by an F-15C from the Massachusetts Air National Guard's 104th Fighter Wing as they entered an Air Defense Identification Zone during the air-defence exercise Operation Noble Defender. US Air National Guard/MSgt Bryan Hoover

B-1B 86-0107 from the 28th Bomb Wing at Dyess AFB, Texas, arriving at RAF Fairford in the UK on October 12, 2023, while supporting a Bomber Task Force Europe mission. USAF/SrA Ryan Hayman

arrived from Ellsworth AFB. The squadron's replacement by the Dyess-based 9th EBS marked the initial deployment of updated IBS/SB-16-equpped B-1Bs.

The first deployment to be fully supported by upgraded bombers began in July 2017, when the 37th arrived. It was relieved by B-52Hs from the 20th EBS, which resumed the CBP rotation in February 2018. In April 2020, the AFGSC concluded its support for the CBP missions in favour of a revised deployment concept known as Bomber Task Forces (BTF). AFGSC's deployment concept supports the National Defense Strategy and the Department of Defense's dynamic force employment concept.

The B-1B's first BTF mission took place when the 7th BW deployed to Andersen just one month after the CBP mission in the Indo-Pacific theatre ended at the base. Intended to be more agile and unpredictable, the BTF concept permits the command to "deliver lethal, ready, long-range strike options to geographic combatant commanders anytime, anywhere."

B-1Bs from the 7th and 28th Bomb Wings share the flightline at Dyess AFB, Texas, on February 1, 2024. The 28th Bomb Wing aircraft normally operate from Ellsworth AFB, South Dakota. USAF/SrA Leon Redfern

Besides short-duration deployments to international operating locations, the BTF concept includes so-called CONUS-to-CONUS missions that see the bombers depart from and return to bases in the US after conducting training in the European, Central or Indo-Pacific Command areas of operation. During May 2020 alone, B-1Bs flying from Ellsworth carried out three long-duration round-trip BTF missions to Europe, where they conducted operations with numerous allied air arms.

Not strictly limited to active component units, the BTF missions have also involved the AFRC, and, in September 2020, three Lancers flown by crews from the 489th BG's 345th EBS at Dyess performed a mission over the East Siberian Sea and recovered at Eielson AFB, Alaska. Over the eight-day period that followed, the bombers conducted 19 missions alongside allied air forces in international airspace throughout the Arctic, including the East Siberian and Norwegian Seas, and as far south as the Sea of Okhotsk between Russia and Japan. ➤

B-1B 86-0103 assigned to the 9th Expeditionary Bomb Squadron rolls down the runway during take-off at RAF Fairford, United Kingdom, at the conclusion of Bomber Task Force deployment 24-1. *USAF/A1C Emma Anderson*

B-1Bs from the 28th Bomb Wing's 34th and 37th Bomb Squadrons share the ramp at Dyess AFB, Texas, on February 1, 2024. USAF/SSgt Holly Cook

In February 2021, B-1Bs from the 7th BW's 9th EBS conducted the first ever BTF deployment to Norway, arriving at Ørland Main Air Station for an extended period of training. According to US European Command, the deployment was intended to give personnel exposure to operations "in the high north [and improve] interoperability with allies and partners across the European theatre."

In early 2024, four B-1Bs from the 7th BW's 9th EBS were deployed for the first time to Morón Air Base in Spain. The missions carried out as part of BTF 24-2 included operations from Luleå-Kallax Air Base in Sweden and a rare visit to Incirlik Air Base, Turkey.

Ongoing upgrades are equipping the Lancer with the Rockwell Collins multifunctional information distribution system joint tactical radio system (MIDS-JTRS) terminal, which provides improved communications and networking. Additionally, the bomber is receiving Mode 5 identification friend-or-foe (IFF) and automatic dependent surveillance broadcast (ADS-B Out) capabilities to ensure it meets domestic and international air traffic mandates.

In June 2018, the fleet was grounded following an emergency landing at Midland International Air and Space Port in Texas following an in-flight engine fire and a failed ejection. Another safety stand-down in March 2019 was caused by an issue with the bomber's ejection system. Heavy combat use in US Central Command during close air support missions came at a cost for the B-1B fleet and, in August 2019, it was reported that as few as six B-1Bs were fully mission-capable. At the time, 39 of the bombers were reportedly grounded for inspections and 15 were receiving depot maintenance.

Originally designed with a service life of 8,000-10,000 hours, in January 2020 the fleet had flown an average of 9,720 hours. The Lancers, like the B-52, have seen their mission set change greatly. Rather than carrying out high-speed, low-level missions, the aircraft spent a great deal of time orbiting at slower speeds and high altitudes, which resulted in stresses being placed on the airframe and wing structures that were not anticipated when the bomber was designed.

Concerned about the structural viability of the aircraft, the USAF reduced annual flight hours for each bomber in order to reduce the stresses on the airframe. The service is awaiting the results of the ongoing fatigue tests that will stress-test airframe and wings to the equivalent of 27,000 and 28,000 flight hours. The results will assist the USAF in determining if the bombers can remain in service until their planned retirement and whether significant repairs to airframes with heavy structural damage are cost-effective.

Although USAF's 2018 Bomber Vector roadmap included plans to retire both the B-1B and B-2A by the early 2030s, the service's FY 2021 budget request called for the removal of 17 "structurally deficient" aircraft from service, reducing the B-1B fleet from 62 to just 45 aircraft. Rather than spending $10-30 million to restore each aircraft, the USAF made the decision to retire the bombers with the least amount of useful life remaining.

A B-1B from the 9th Expeditionary Bomb Squadron is prepared for a mission in support of Bomber Task Force Europe at Morón Air Base, Spain, on April 4, 2024. USAF/SrA Zachary Wright

Wearing special markings as the flagship of the 7th Bomb Wing, B-1B 86-0117 departs Morón Air Base, Spain, during Bomber Task Force 24-2, on April 15, 2024. USAF/Sgt Megan M. Beatty

A B-1B from the 37th Expeditionary Bomb Squadron taxies at Andersen AFB, Guam, at the start of a mission on June 13, 2024. USAF/A1C Dylan Maher

The 2021 National Defense Authorization Act (NDAA) partially approved that plan but required the USAF to maintain four of the retired bombers in Type 2000 'recallable storage' to ensure they could return to service if required. The first bomber retired under the USAF's congressionally approved divesture plan was delivered to the 309th AMARG at Davis-Monthan AFB, Arizona on February 17, when serial 85-0066 arrived from Ellsworth.

The retirements were completed in September 2021, but only 13 of the Bones were placed in storage with the 309th AMARG. In accordance with the Bomber Capability Roadmap, funds saved by retiring the aircraft are being redirected to investments intended to combat obsolescence and diminishing manufacturing sources.

Whereas most of the bombers were placed in long term Type 4000 storage, four were held in Type 2000 'recallable storage'. Of the remaining aircraft, examples went to Tinker AFB in Oklahoma as a prototype for structural repairs, to Edwards AFB as a ground-based test asset, to Wichita State University's National Institute for Aviation Research in Kansas for digital mapping, and to Barksdale AFB in Louisiana as a static display for the Barksdale Global Power Museum.

The NDAA required the air force to maintain an operational fleet of 92 combat-coded bombers, comprising the B-1B, B-52H and B-2A, and restricted the service from reducing the number of personnel assigned to maintain the remaining Lancers. Savings resulting from the B-1B retirements have been used by the USAF to provide the 45 remaining bombers with structural repairs and modifications required to keep them viable until the B-21A is fielded and the Bones are finally retired sometime in the mid-2030s or later.

On April 20, 2022, B-1B serial 85-0089 operated by the 7th Bomb Wing experienced a catastrophic engine failure during routine maintenance at Dyess Air Force Base, Texas. The USAF is congressionally mandated to maintain an inventory of 45 B-1Bs. However, because the projected repair costs to restore the fire-damaged aircraft were determined to be prohibitive, the USAF's Strategic Plans and Programs office made the decision to regenerate one of the four Lancers bombers from Type 2000 storage in Arizona.

As a result, B-1B serial 85-0081 was reactivated. On February 8, 2024, the bomber departed Davis-Monthan and was flown to Tinker AFB, Oklahoma, where "heavy restoration and maintenance" is being carried out by the 76th Aircraft Maintenance Group's 567th Aircraft Maintenance Squadron.

The loss of another B-1B during a landing mishap at Ellsworth on January 4, 2024, caused the USAF to reactivate another aircraft from storage and serial 86-0115 was flown to Tinker AFB, on July 2, 2024.

According to a statement made to the US Senate Armed Services Committee's Subcommittee on Strategic Forces, General Thomas A Bussiere, commander of Air Force Global Strike Command on May 22, 2024: "Until the B-21 Raider fleet is fully fielded, the B-1 will continue to play a prominent role in USAF global power projection." ∎

A 37th Expeditionary Bomb Squadron B-1B departs Andersen AFB, Guam, on June 13, 2024, in support of a Bomber Task Force mission. USAF/SSgt Jake Jacobsen

Spirit in the sky

509th Bomb Wing insignia

Tasked with both conventional and nuclear missions, the Northrop Grumman B-2A is the USAF's only long-range strike aircraft capable of penetrating advanced integrated air defence systems and delivering weapons against heavily defended targets. In addition to its nuclear deterrence mission, the bomber's intercontinental range and low observable profile give it the ability to conduct nuclear response, global strikes, and precision attack missions. The B-2A has served as the USAF's primary penetrating nuclear-capable bomber since achieving full operational capability in 2003 and is projected to remain in front-line service-until 2030 or beyond.

Production and upgrades

Development of the Advanced Technology Bomber (ATB) began in 1979, with the USAF issuing a formal request for proposals in September 1980. Northrop was selected to develop the ATB in October 1981 and initially received a $7.3 billion contract to build two structural test airframes, one flying prototype and five evaluation aircraft.

Publicly displayed for the first time in November 1988, when it was rolled out in Palmdale, California, the aircraft incorporated a high degree of low-observable (LO) technologies. Providing the bomber with the ability to penetrate heavily defended enemy defences and deliver a wide variety of nuclear and conventional weapons, the LO characteristics result from a combination of reduced infrared, acoustic, electromagnetic, visual and radar signatures. A unique combination of range, precision, payload, and ability to operate in anti-access/area denial (A2/AD) environments permits the B-2 to identify, locate, target, and destroy the highest value enemy targets.

First flown at Air Force Plant 42 in Palmdale, California, on July 18, 1989, six developmental B-2As (AV-1/6) eventually supported the flight test programme and all were later refurbished and entered operational service. The first example was delivered to the 509th Bomb Wing (BW) at Whiteman AFB, Missouri, on December 17, 1993, and the 393rd Bomb Squadron (BS) flew its maiden training sortie just five days later. Initial operational capability (IOC) was achieved in April 1997 and delivery of the last of 21 bombers occurred in 2000.

Plans originally called for the acquisition of 132 B-2s, but the number was reduced to 75 in 1990 following a Department of Defense Major Aircraft Review, and finally to 20 in addition to the prototype. US lawmakers eventually authorised funding that allowed the conversion of the first test vehicle into a combat aircraft.

The developmental bombers were followed by ten Block 10 models (AV7/16) that were delivered between December 1993 and January 1996. The Block 10 configuration offered a limited combat capability that included conventional 2000lb Mk84 general purpose (GP) bombs or B61 and B83 nuclear gravity nuclear weapons. IOC was achieved in April 1997.

The Block 20 configured aircraft followed from May 1996, featuring an interim capability to deliver GPS aided munitions (GAM). The Block 20's GPS-aided targeting system (GATS) allowed

Spirit of Pennsylvania, one of three B-2As that conducted a mission against targets in Libya, returns to Whiteman AFB, Missouri, on March 20, 2011. USAF/SrA Kenny Holston

it to deploy precision-guided 2,000lb GBU-36/Bs and 4,700lb GBU-37/B GAMs. Each aircraft was capable of carrying 16 GBU-36s or eight of the larger bombs. Developed specifically for the B-2A and produced in limited numbers, the weapons were later replaced by GPS-guided joint direct attack munitions (JDAMs). The GATS worked in conjunction with the Raytheon AN/APQ-181's synthetic aperture radar mode and a GPS receiver to determine target co-ordinates for the GAMs.

Certified to operate at a maximum take-off weight of 336,500lb, the Block 20 provided a limited terrain following/terrain avoidance (TF/TA) capability that allowed the aircraft to fly at altitudes as low as 600ft. The first Block 20 aircraft, AV18, was delivered to the 509th BW on May 15, 1996, and the variant achieved IOC for both nuclear and conventional warfare missions on April 1, 1997. Three aircraft, AV-17/19, were produced in Block 20 configuration and five Block 10 models, AV12-16, were updated to that configuration. The Block 20 variant achieved IOC for both nuclear and conventional warfare missions on April 1, 1997, and the last of three aircraft was delivered the following month.

The first of two production Block 30s (AV20) flew at Palmdale on April 15, 1997, and was delivered to Whiteman on August 7, 1997. Structural modifications, radar cross section (RCS) and radar absorbent material (RAM) coating improvements were incorporated on these. The aircraft also featured full JDAM integration and incorporated bomb rack assembly units that enabled the carriage of CBU-87 cluster munitions, aerial mines, and other smaller stores. Additionally, a MILSTAR satellite communications terminal was

Flown by a crew from the 419th Flight Test Squadron, Spirit of New York *conducts flight tests above Rogers Dry Lake on Edwards AFB, California, on August 3, 2023.* USAF/Giancarlo Casem

incorporated and the defence management subsystem (DMS) achieved full capability. Enhancements to the Raytheon AN/APQ-181 radar included a ground moving-target indication (GMTI) mode and TF/TA capabilities that allowed the aircraft to fly as low as 200ft. Block 30 conversions began in Palmdale in July 1995 and the final upgraded aircraft, AV1,

was delivered in July 2000. Six development models, five Block 10s and eight Block 20s were all converted to Block 30 configuration in Palmdale. The B-2A achieved full operational capability on December 17, 2003.

Since entering service, the fleet has received many upgrades and recent programmes have equipped the B-2A with additional weapons, new communications capabilities and upgraded radar. The AN/APQ-181 multi-mode radar was updated as part of the B-2 Radar Modernization Program (RMP) that began in 2002. It replaced the system's passive electronically scanned antennas (ESA) with a Ku-band active electronically scanned array (AESA) antenna and resolved potential conflicts in radio frequency ➤

A pilot from the 13th Bomb Squadron directs the crew of B-2A 88-0329 to a parking spot at Andersen AFB, Guam on June 13, 2024. USAF/SSgt Kristen Heller

usage between the bomber and commercial satellite systems that utilised the same frequency spectrum.

Flight testing of the new radar began aboard aircraft AV-3 in April 2006, after the B-2 Combined Test Force (CTF) completed initial radar-subsystem integration and acceptance testing. The first aircraft to be equipped with the modified radar as part of the RMP system development and demonstration (SDD) phase was returned to the USAF on March 17, 2009. Northrop Grumman had received a $468 million contract associated with the production phase in December 2008. Installation of the radar in the last of five SDD aircraft was completed at Whiteman in November 2009. Low rate initial production (LRIP) began in November 2008 and full rate production started in November 2009. Northrop Grumman completed the last of 13 production RMP installations in September 2012.

Subsequent major upgrades incorporated a new satellite communications system, computers, and additional weapons capabilities, as well as upgrades to the DMS. Although DMS modernisation (DMS-M) was once the USAF's number one priority for the B-2 fleet, the project was scaled back in 2021. Expected to cost around $310.9 million, the programme was intended to resolve the B-2 fleet's top obsolescence issue and improve sustainability, including upgrades for the electronic support measures, passive antennas and display processing units that comprise the bomber's electronic warfare system. Ultimately, the programme was eventually scaled back to just cockpit displays and display processors. The current B-2 display modernisation (BDM)

programme upgrades the primary cockpit displays and installs fully integrated multi-function display units (MDUs).

The B-2 Extremely High Frequency Satellite Communications (EHF SATCOM) and Computer Increment 1 programme (B-2 EHF Inc 1) replaced the ultra-high frequency (UHF) communications equipment with an EHF SATCOM system compatible with both the legacy EHF satellite (MILSTAR I/II) systems and the future advanced extremely high frequency (AEHF) SATCOM systems. It provided a new integrated processing unit (IPU), upgraded flight management computer processors, increased data storage, a re-hosted flight management operational flight programme (OFP) and a high bandwidth databus that supports the EHF SATCOM installation and provides the growth required for future upgrades.

The systems were certified as compatible for nuclear operations on April 2, 2013, and Air Force Global Strike Command authorised fielding and conventional and nuclear use of EHF-modified aircraft on April 26, 2013. The first production installation began in November 2013 and full rate production (FRP) was approved in July 2014. Plans for follow-on increments 2 and 3 were cancelled.

Northrop Grumman developed and integrated the flexible strike (Flex Strike) software upgrade, which will serve as the basis for future system enhancements, including the ability to carry multiple weapon types. Previously known as the stores management operational flight programme (SMOFP) re-host and mixed carriage modification, Flex Strike Phase 1 (FS-1) provided the bomber with an expanded processing capability. Additionally, it enabled

the aircraft to carry a mixed weapons load with a rotary launcher assembly (RLA) in one weapons bay and a smart bomb rack assembly (SBRA) in the other and enabled full integration of the B61-12 life extension programme (LEP) upgrades.

Northrop Grumman started work on the three-year engineering and manufacturing development (EMD) portion of the project when it received an $102 million contract in August 2014. The software upgrades reduced maintenance costs and improved mission flexibility and aircraft reliability and provided the aircraft with a single OFP that replaced several mission-specific software versions.

Installation of the common very low frequency receiver (CVR) improved the aircrew's ability to receive strategic communication messages. It integrated a receive-only, very low bandwidth VLF receiver and antenna subsystem that delivered a secure, survivable strategic nuclear communication capability.

The B-2 advanced communications programme includes integration of the latest version of the adaptable communications suite (ACS 4.0) that provides Link 16-based jam-resistant in-flight retasking, advanced Identification friend-or-foe (IFF) mode 5/S and updates intended to comply with cryptographic mandates.

ACS is a non-integrated system that provides SATCOM connectivity for command and control en route to the target. It provides the ability to receive airborne mission transfer (AMT) and beyond-line-of-sight (BLOS) situational awareness. Improvements to the B-2's UHF communications system updates BLOS capabilities via the multiple user objective system (MUOS) satellite constellation. The associated airborne integrated terminal group (AITG) provides LOS UHF communications and VHF anti-jam, encrypted and unencrypted voice communications. B-2 battlespace collaborative combat communications (B2C3) will enable operation in the advanced battle management system (ABMS) and joint all-domain command and control (JADC2) environment. Development began in October 2022 and fielding is expected to begin during 2024. B2C3 is a compilation of multiple efforts designed to provide the Spirit with open mission systems (OMS) architecture.

The B-2 display modernisation (BDM) programme will replace the B-2A's eight MDUs that serve as the aircraft's primary cockpit displays. Combined developmental test and evaluation (DTE) and initial operational test and evaluation (IOT&E) and operational test and evaluation (OTE) is planned for early and ▸

595th 131st Bomb Wing insignia

6T-38A 67-14826 operates with Spirit of South Carolina during a training mission over Whiteman AFB, Missouri, on February 20, 2014. USAF/SSgt Jonathan Snyder

mid-2025. A host of smaller upgrades that will improve safety, reliability, maintainability and/or improve system performance are under way as well, to ensure that the Spirit remains viable until it reaches the end of its projected service life.

Low observable signature and supportability modifications (LOSSMs) and aircraft supportability modifications (ASMs) implement improvements designed to slow signature degradation and to improve LO supportability. Associated projects include structural modifications and improvements to coatings, materials, and radar-absorptive structures such as the radome and engine inlets/exhausts, to provide advanced signature reduction, reduce LO maintenance and improve aircraft availability and survivability. Additionally, structural and avionics modifications to improve the performance of the aircraft and engines and reduce maintenance and logistics requirements are also being studied.

Airframe hardware supportability modifications (AHSMs) will increase aircraft availability by addressing current and forecasted obsolescence issues for a variety of systems, including communications, radar components, flight control computer and propulsion system equipment.

In addition, low cost upgrades that address safety, reliability, maintainability, and/or improved system performance issues are being implemented, as are low-cost modifications

to provide the bomber's 19,000lb-st F118-GE-100 engine with a service life extension and enhance engine reliability and performance.

Combat missions

The Spirit's combat debut occurred over Kosovo on March 24, 1999, on the initial night of Operation Allied Force. Over 35 days, six B-2As flew 47 combat sorties from Whiteman AFB that averaged 31 hours in length. Although responsible for less than 1% of the total sorties flown, the B-2As delivered 656 weapons, totalling 1.3 million pounds, and destroyed 11% of the fixed targets in Serbia and Kosovo.

Following the 9-11 terror attacks on New York and Washington DC, B-2As were the first aircraft to attack targets in Afghanistan during the initial days of Operation Enduring Freedom. From October 6-11, 2001, six 44+ hour missions were flown from Whiteman and crews delivered a total of 64 weapons against targets in Afghanistan, before recovering at Naval Support Facility Diego Garcia, British Indian Ocean Territory (BIOT). Engine running crew changes (ERCC) were conducted during several missions and a second crew flew the 29-hour return flight to Whiteman. The ERCC involved the bomber's single longest missions, two sorties lasting 73 hours.

The aircraft flew its first missions in support of Operation Iraqi Freedom from Whiteman on March 21, 2003. Nine aircraft were involved, and the bomber's first combat deployment saw four B-2As fly sorties from Diego Garcia. By April

8, the bombers had delivered 676 GPS-guided JDAM, GBU-37 GPS-aided munitions (GAMs) and unguided 500lb bombs totalling 1.5 million pounds against around 600 individual targets during 41 missions.

On March 21, 2011, three B-2As delivered 45 weapons that destroyed hardened aircraft shelters on a Libyan airfield in support of the United Nations no-fly zone over Libya at the start of Operation Odyssey Dawn. Each of the 25+ hour 11,418m round trips originated at Whiteman.

The bombers most recently saw combat on October 17, 2024, when B-2As struck Houthi targets in Yemen, marking the first time the Spirit had been used against the Iranian-backed group. The mission was designed to degrade the group's ability to disrupt global shipping in the Red Sea, Gulf of Aden, and Bab El-Mandeb Strait. The bombers reportedly struck five hardened underground weapons storage locations that contained missiles, weapons components and other munitions used to target military and civilian vessels in the region.

Weapons

In addition to its nuclear deterrence mission, the bomber's intercontinental range and low observable profile provide the capability to conduct nuclear response, global strike, and global precision attack missions. Capable of precisely delivering nearly 60,000lb of conventional and nuclear ordnance, the bomber has an unrefuelled range of around

A B-2A is flanked by a pair of T-38As in preparations for a flyover during the 2019 Wings over Whiteman Air & Space Show at Whiteman AFB, Missouri, on June 15, 2019. USAF/TSgt Alexander W Riedel

6,000nm and can fly up to 10,000nm with a single aerial refuelling.

Each of the B-2A's two side-by-side weapon bays is capable of carrying up to 30,000lb of ordnance on eight-round rotary launcher assemblies (RLAs). Alternately, four smart bomb rack assemblies (SBRAs) allow the bomber to engage as many as 80 separate targets. Development of the SBRA began in January 2001 and the programme was completed in March 2006 when the 54th unit was delivered. For conventional missions, the bomber can carry 16 GBU-31 JDAMs, 80 GBU-38 JDAMs, 36 CBU-87/89/97 cluster bombs, 16 AGM-154 joint stand-off weapons (JSOW) or AGM-158 joint air-to-surface stand-off missiles (JASSMs), eight GBU-28, GBU-37 or EGBU-28 5,000lb penetrator bombs or a pair of 30,000lb GBU-57 massive ordnance penetrators (MOPs). For the nuclear mission, up to 16 B61 or B83 free-fall nuclear bombs can be carried.

MOP integration provided the B-2A with the ability to deliver the GBU-57, which is designed for use against hardened, deeply buried targets. Work to integrate the weapon began in July 2007 and the B-2A is the only long-range, penetrating A2/AD platform capable of carrying the bunker-buster. As part of the MOP integration, the aircraft's GPS antenna was upgraded to allow the transmission of enhanced signals to weapons loaded on the SBRAs and RLAs prior to release.

The previously mentioned Flex Strike 1 programme gave the B-2A the capability ▶

B-2A 82-1068 from the 509th Bomb Wing conducts aerial refuelling operations with a KC-135R Stratotanker assigned to the 100th Air Refueling Wing over the North Sea. USAF/TSgt Matthew Plew

A pair of B-2As assigned to the 509th Bomb Wing conducting aerial operations over the North Sea while supporting Bomber Task Force Europe 20-2 on March 12, 2020. USAF/MSgt Matthew Plew

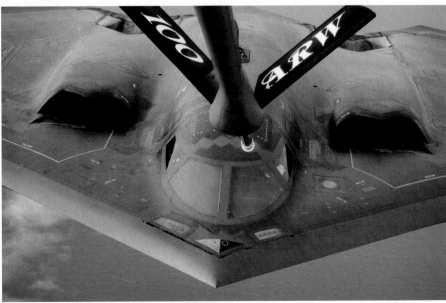

A B-2A from the 509th Bomb Wing conducts aerial refuelling operations during a Bomber Task Force mission over the Atlantic. USAF/SSgt Rachel Maxwell

B-2A 93-1086 operated by the 393rd Expeditionary Bomb Squadron takes off from Royal Australian Air Force Base Amberley, Australia, as part of a Bomber Task Force mission, on August 19, 2024. USAF/MSgt Kenneth W Norman

to be configured with multiple weapons and provided the bomber with maximum strategic nuclear and conventional strike flexibility. New weapons included the B61-12 precision-guided thermonuclear freefall weapon, advanced versions of the GBU-28E/B and GBU-28B/D bunker busters, AGM-158A JASSMs and extended range AGM-158B JASSM-ERs, a 5000lb version of JDAM, a 2,000lb GBU-56 laser JDAM (L/JDAM), a GBU-53/B small diameter bomb II and the planned AGM-181 long-range stand-off (LRSO) cruise missile.

The B-2 is receiving another significant upgrade through the Spirit Realm 1 (SR 1) initiative. This upgrade enhances the aircraft's

communications and weapon systems, via multi mission domain (MMD) open mission systems architecture. In addition to directly enhancing the bomber's capability, SR 1 allows a new phase of agile software releases to be easily integrated. The initiative features new flight hardware, displays, and updates that make the aircraft more survivable.

The B-2 achieved another milestone recently with the integration of a radar aided targeting system (RATS). This enables delivery of the modern B61-12 by using the aircraft's radar to guide the weapon in GPS-denied conditions. The bomber successfully dropped an inert B61-12 using RATS on June 14, 2022. Additionally, it successfully employed

the long-range AGM-158B JASSM-ER cruise missile for the first time in a test launch in December 2021.

During the Rim of the Pacific (RIMPAC) 2024 exercise, a B-2A demonstrated another capability when it contributed to the sinking of the ex-USS *Dubuque* (LPD 8) using GPS-guided bombs. Conducted on July 11, 2024, the mission demonstrated the bomber's ability to engage maritime targets with low-cost, GPS-guided weapons. Funded by the Office of the Under Secretary of Defense for Research and Engineering, the so-called Quicksink experiment was intended to "provide options to neutralise surface maritime threats while demonstrating the inherent flexibility of the joint force."

Spirit of South Carolina *makes a low pass over Hill AFB, Utah, during the Warriors Over the Wasatch airshow in 2024.* USAF/SrA Jack Rodgers

Air Vehicle	Serial	Name	Delivery Date	Notes
AV-1	82-1066	*Spirit of America*	14 Jul 00	
AV-2	82-1067	*Spirit of Arizona*	20 Mar 98	
AV-3	82-1068	*Spirit of New York*	7 Oct 97	Damaged in mishap Whiteman AFB Dec.10, 2022
AV-4	82-1069	*Spirit of Indiana*	22 May 99	
AV-5	82-1070	*Spirit of Ohio*	18 Jul 97	
AV-6	82-1071	*Spirit of Mississippi*	23 May 98	
AV-7	88-0328	*Spirit of Texas*	31 Aug 94	
AV-8	88-0329	*Spirit of Missouri*	17 Dec 93	
AV-9	88-0330	*Spirit of California*	17 Aug 94	
AV-10	88-0331	*Spirit of South Carolina*	30 Dec 94	
AV-11	88-0332	*Spirit of Washington*	30 Oct 94	Damaged by engine fire at Andersen AFB, Guam Feb. 26, 2010. Returned to service Dec. 16, 2013.
AV-12	89-0127	*Spirit of Kansas*	15 Feb 95	Crashed at Andersen AFB, Guam Feb. 23, 2008.
AV-13	89-0128	*Spirit of Nebraska*	28 Jun 95	
AV-14	89-0129	*Spirit of Georgia*	17 Nov 95	
AV-15	90-0040	*Spirit of Alaska*	24 Jan 96	
AV-16	90-0041	*Spirit of Hawaii*	11 Jan 96	
AV-17	92-0700	*Spirit of Florida*	3 Jul 96	
AV-18	93-1085	*Spirit of Oklahoma*	15 May 96	
AV-19	93-1086	*Spirit of Kitty Hawk*	30 Aug 96	
AV-20	93-1087	*Spirit of Pennsylvania*	5 Aug 97	Assigned to test duties at Edwards AFB, California
AV-21	93-1088	*Spirit of Louisiana*	10 Nov 97	

Operations

Originally assigned to Air Combat Command (ACC), the B-2 fleet has been controlled by the US Global Strike Command via the Eighth Air Force since February 2010. Stationed at Whiteman AFB since September 30, 1990, the 509th BW is responsible for the combat-coded B-2A fleet. The operational fleet of 18 B-2As is assigned to the wing's 509th Operations Group (OG) and flown by the 393rd BS. Only 16 B-2As are maintained as combat-ready aircraft at any given time. The wing's 13th BS is tasked as the formal training unit (FTU). Previously tasked as an operational squadron, it assumed the schoolhouse mission in April 2018, when the 394th Combat Training Squadron was inactivated. The squadron utilises 14 Northrop Grumman T-38As as companion trainers, which provide Spirit pilots with the ability to conduct multiple sorties each month. The Talons allow pilots to maintain basic flying proficiency, airmanship and real-time decision-making skills at low cost compared to the B-2A. In addition to operational B-2As, instructions are supported by several training aids that include weapon systems and mission and cockpit procedures trainers.

Operations are also conducted by the Missouri Air National Guard's 131st BW and its assigned 110th BS, which shares the responsibility for operating and maintaining the bombers under a classic reserve association. The classic associate unit transitioned from the F-15 to the B-2A in 2007 and relocated from St Louis International Airport to Whiteman as part of the USAF's Total Force Integration (TFI) programme. On June 18, 2008, the wing achieved a major milestone when it completed the first B-2A sortie to be launched and flown by Air National Guard personnel. It later became the first Air National Guard unit certified to conduct the nuclear mission upon completion of an Initial Nuclear Security Inspection in August 2013.

The two bomb wings completed the first TFI combat mission over Libya on March 21, 2011 when three B-2s delivered 45 2,000lb GBU-31 JDAMs that destroyed hardened aircraft shelters at an air base near Sirte, during an 11,418 mile round-trip mission in support of Operation 'Odyssey Dawn'.

Since entering the service, the B-2A fleet has flown more than 120,000 hours, including more than 3,000 in combat over Kosovo and in support of Operations Enduring Freedom, Iraqi Freedom, and Odyssey Dawn.

Bomber Task Force

Beginning in 2005, the B-2A supported US Pacific Command's Continuous Bomber Presence (CBP) by conducting scheduled rotations to Andersen AFB, Guam. In August 2012, the AFGSC announced that B-2As would begin regular worldwide training deployments to each of the regional US Combatant Command's areas of responsibility during 2013. The plan called for small numbers ▶

Spirit of New York *taxies in preparation for take-off during exercise Spirit Vigilance at Whiteman AFB on November 7, 2022.*
USAF/A1C Bryson Britt

Companion Trainers

The Accelerated Co-Pilot Enrichment (ACE) programme was created under the Strategic Air Command (SAC) and was designed to permit bomber and tanker co-pilots to build flight time. In addition to flying experience, the programme's objective is to strengthen the co-pilot's self-confidence and develop their judgment and decision-making skills. The ACE programmes were an essential part of the co-pilot's preparation to assume aircraft commander responsibilities in their primary mission aircraft. The programme utilised Cessna T-37Bs and Northrop T-38As detached from Air Training Command (ATC) Flying Training Wings (FTW).

Under Air Combat Command, the ACE programme became known as the Companion Trainer Program (CTP) and bomber bases continued to utilise the T-37Bs and T-38As in a similar role. The programme was later reduced in scope and today around 50 T-38As continue to serve with units of the Air Combat (ACC) and Air Force Global Strike Commands (AFGSC) Command. Talons in service with the latter comprise 14 T-38As assigned to the B-2A equipped 509th Bomb Wing (BW) at Whiteman Air Force Base, Missouri.

Tasked as the B-2A Formal Training Unit (FTU), the 509th BW's 13th Bomb Squadron (BS) has been responsible for the T-38As since the 394th Combat Training Squadron was inactivated in April 2018.

First fielded in March 1961, the supersonic Talons allow B-2A pilots to maintain their qualifications and basic flying proficiency, airmanship and their real-time decision-making skills at low cost when compared to the bombers.

B-2A 82-1067 lifts off at the start of a Bomber Task Force mission at Royal Australian Air Force Base Amberley, Australia, on September 11, 2024. USAF/SSgt Whitney Erhart

Training

The B-2 training system provides initial qualification, proficiency, continuation, re-qualification, mission rehearsal and upgrade training for B-2 aircrew, maintainers, and weapons loaders. Four cockpit procedures trainers consist of a full-scale cockpit that enables aircrews to become proficient on aircraft systems operations and procedures. Three full-motion weapon systems trainers (WST) support initial and continuation aircrew training and allow crews to become proficient in operating the aircraft and its weapon systems under simulated combat situations. The WSTs also support mission rehearsal training prior to an actual combat sortie launch. Spirit pilots typically fly ten hours in a B-2A and six hours in a T-38A each month and spend four hours in a simulator. Because they can undergo emergencies and potential enemy threats, the simulator delivers higher-fidelity training than the actual aircraft. The system's electronic combat environment is capable of providing up to 12,000 threats per mission, including radar emitters, surface-to-air missiles, anti-aircraft batteries and other jets.

In addition to those devices used by the flight crew, the B-2 Training System includes around 50 devices that provide maintenance and weapons loading experience.

Test and evaluation

Testing associated with B-2A is conducted by several squadrons assigned to Air Force Materiel Command (AFMC) and Air Combat Command (ACC) rather than AFGSC. Development testing is the responsibility of the 412th Test Wing's 419th Flight Test Squadron at Edwards AFB, California, which is assigned to the Air Force Test Center and operates a single B-2A. The 'Global Bombers' test squadron operates examples of the B-1B and B-52H. B-2A serial 93-1087, which carries the name *Spirit of Pennsylvania* returned to Edwards on July 17, 2024, in advance of the start of testing associated with the integration of an open mission systems architecture, under the previously mentioned Spirit Realm 1.

Also located at Edwards, the 31st Test & Evaluation Squadron (TES) is a geographically

of aircraft to rotate to forward operating locations for short periods. A recent Bomber Task Force (BTF) mission was carried out by crews from the 509th BW and 131st BW, which deployed three Spirits to Royal Australian Air Force (RAAF) Base Amberley in Queensland from August 16 to September 17, 2024. The crews conducted familiarisation training activities in the Indo-Asia-Pacific region, participated in several joint multinational training events and made a visit to Diego Garcia, where they conducted hot pit refuelling operations. During this time, the bombers, which were assigned to the 110th Expeditionary Bomb Squadron, flew 37 sorties totalling 341 hours.

Also stationed at Whiteman, the 325th Weapons Squadron (WPS) is a geographically separated unit (GSU) of ACC's 57th Wing and the USAF Weapons School at Nellis AFB, Nevada. Utilising aircraft assigned to the host wing, the 325th provides advanced 'graduate-level' training in weapons and tactics employment. It has been stationed at Whiteman since September 2005, when it replaced the 715th WPS.

B-2A 82-1071 is prepared for a mission at Andersen AFB, Guam, while a KC-135R departs from the base on August 15, 2016. USAF/SrA Jovan Banks

A B-2A from the 509th Bomb Wing operates with an F-15C assigned to the 48th Fighter Wing over the North Sea on September 16, 2019. USAF/TSgt Matthew Plew

A T-38A from the 509th bomb Wing at Whiteman AFB, Missouri, taxies at Scott AFB, Illinois during a refuelling stop on April 28, 2015. USAF/SrA Tristin Englis

separated unit (GSU) of the 53rd Wing's 53rd Test and Evaluation Group (TEG). The ACC-assigned unit is tasked with conducting combined test and evaluation and uses the B-2A assigned to the 419th FLTS. Located at Whiteman, the 72nd TES is also a GSU of the 53rd TEG. It conducts operational test and evaluation of the B-2A using aircraft assigned to the host wing.

Logistical support

Although managed by the Oklahoma City Air Logistics Complex at Tinker AFB, Oklahoma, B-2A depot maintenance and major modifications are typically carried by Northrop Grumman at its Aircraft Integration Center of Excellence in Palmdale, California. In May 2024, the contractor received a five-year, indefinite delivery/indefinite quantity Flexible Acquisition

Sustainment Team (FAST) III contract valued at up to $7.2 billion under which it provides support and modernisation for the Spirit fleet. Under the terms of the contract, Northrop Grumman's efforts include contract depot maintenance (CDM), consolidated delivery order (CDO) and integrated contractor support (ICS).

Whereas each B-2A had previously undergone programmed depot maintenance (PDM) in Palmdale every seven years, the overhaul cycle was extended to nine years as part of an effort to increase the bomber's availability. The effort also reduced the average PDM time from more than 400 days to 365 days. Additionally, a savings of around $900 million in maintenance costs will be realised over the life of the fleet.

While PDM and major modification efforts are conducted at Palmdale, smaller projects are carried out locally at Whiteman. A number of ongoing projects are currently being carried out under the FAST and other contracts.

Deployment sites

Whereas the B-2A fleet operates from permanent climate-controlled hangars at Whiteman, FOLs at Andersen AFB in Guam and RAF Fairford in Gloucestershire, England, deployable, environmentally controlled hangars support operations at Diego Garcia when required. Known as the B-2 Shelter System (B2SS) or Extra Large Deployable Aircraft Hangar System (XLDAHS) the structures are 250ft wide, 126ft deep and 55 ft high and can sustain winds up to 110mph.

Losses

Since entering service, one B-2A was written-off in an accident when the *Spirit of Kansas* crashed during take-off at Andersen AFB on February 28, 2008. Fortunately, both pilots ejected safely. A second aircraft was heavily damaged by a ground fire during engine start that also occurred at Andersen on February 26, 2010. *Spirit of Kansas* was subsequently repaired at a cost of more than $105 million and returned to service in December 2013.

On December 10, 2022, *Spirit of New York* was damaged in a mishap at Whiteman following an emergency landing. Although damage was significant, the aircraft was eventually repaired and returned to service.

Naming the Spirits

The B-2A was formally named the Spirit during ceremonies held at Northrop Grumman's Palmdale, California, final assembly facility on March 31, 1994, when AV-9 was christened the *Spirit of California*. ∎

A pair of B-2As taxi prior to take-off at Whiteman AFB, Missouri during exercise Spirit Vigilance on November 7, 2022. USAF/A1C Bryson Britt

Stealthy Raider

The first B-21A Raider was formally unveiled at a ceremony at Northrop Grumman's facility adjacent to Air Force Plant 42 in Palmdale, California, on December 2, 2022. US Air Force

After a relatively short eight-year development period, the USAF is preparing to field the first new long-range bomber developed since the Northrop Grumman B-2A entered service more than 30 years ago. The first flight of the service's new B-21A long-range nuclear-capable bomber took place on November 10, 2023, just 12 days short of the 25th anniversary of the B-2A Spirit's formal rollout.

The first B-21A was publicly unveiled earlier at the Palmdale, facility on December 2, 2022. Carried out from the contractor's facility adjacent to the Air Force Plant 42 Production Flight Test Installation, the flight began just as the sun rose at 0651hrs local time. It concluded

around one hour and 40 minutes later, when the Raider landed at nearby Edwards Air Force Base (AFB). The aircraft carried the name *Cerberus* and a silhouette of the three-headed hound that, according to Greek mythology, guarded the gates of the underworld. During the rollout, then USAF Chief of Staff Gen Charles Q Brown Jr described the B-21A as "a high cycle aircraft", which means it will be capable of flying more sorties at a higher frequency than other aircraft.

Although no specifics were provided about the bomber's range, Secretary of Defense Lloyd Austin said it would allow the bomber "to strike anywhere in the world without needing

to be forward based." When describing its capabilities, Assistant Secretary of the Air Force for Acquisition, Technology and Logistics Andrew P Hunter said, "What we're seeing with the B-21 Raider is a fielding of a long-range penetrating capability that will allow us to carry out our missions in the Indo-Pacific theatre, and in all parts of the world where the Air Force needs to operate and provide the capability the joint force requires."

Prior to the formal unveiling, little information was provided about the Raider. Although renderings of the bomber released in February 2016, confirmed the similarity of its flying wing configuration to the earlier B-2A.

Again, like the B-2A, the Raider will be tasked with conventional and nuclear roles and capable of delivering both stand-off and direct attack munitions. Optimised to defeat anti-access, area-denial systems found in high-end threat environments, the bomber will be capable of penetrating and surviving in advanced air defence environments.

Primary weapons will include the classified AGM-181 long-range stand-off (LRSO) nuclear missile that will succeed the AGM-86B air-launched cruise missile and equip both the B-52J and the B-21A. The LRSO missile is being developed by RTX's Raytheon Technologies, which was selected in 2020 even before the ⯈

A close-up view of the cockpit of the B-21A. Designed for supportability and maintainability, the Raider features an open systems architecture. US Air Force

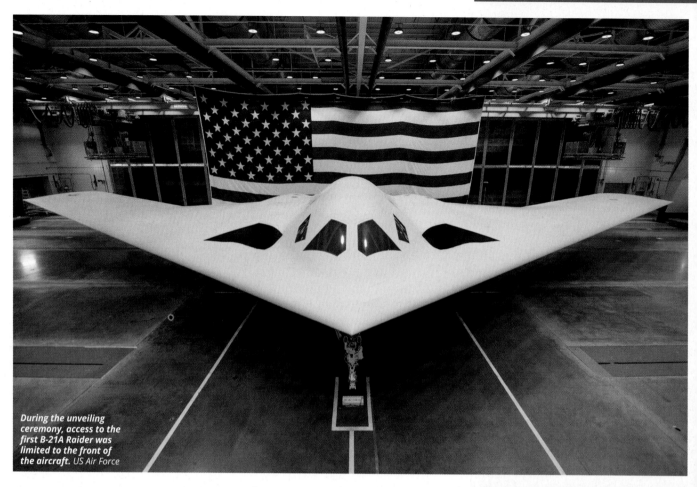

During the unveiling ceremony, access to the first B-21A Raider was limited to the front of the aircraft. US Air Force

programme's technology maturation and risk reduction (TMRR) phase had concluded. The LRSO is expected to be operational on the B-52 by the end of the decade.

Next-Generation Bomber

The Raider's roots can be traced to the USAF's Next-Generation Bomber (NGB) program, which began in 2004 as an initiative to explore new technologies. Initially projected to enter service around 2018, the NGB was envisioned as a stealthy, subsonic, medium-range, medium payload bomber. Although Northrop Grumman and a team composed of Boeing and Lockheed Martin were developing designs, a change in direction caused by budgetary restrictions and nuclear arms treaty considerations resulted in the cancellation of the programme in 2010.

Long-Range Strike Bomber

Following cancellation of the NGB, the USAF and Department of Defense (DoD) considered a number of concepts to accomplish the long-range strike mission. However, after considering the options, the USAF's request to continue developing an optionally manned penetrating bomber was approved in 2011. The long-range strike bomber (LRS-B) differed from the NGB in being more ambitious and expensive. Key capabilities included a large, flexible payload bay capable of carrying a full range of current and future long-range weapons.

A request for proposal (RFP) to develop the LRS-B was issued on July 9, 2014. At that time Secretary of the Air Force Deborah Lee James said: "The LRS-B will be an adaptable and highly capable system based upon mature technology." Intended as a long-range, air-refuellable, highly survivable aircraft with

significant nuclear and conventional stand-off and direct-attack weapons payload, the LRS-B would provide operational flexibility across a wide range of military operations. According to then Air Force Chief of Staff General Mark Welsh: "The long-range strike bomber will be essential to our ability to win a full-spectrum conflict in the future. It is a must-have capability." The RFP specified plans to purchase 80-100 bombers.

Although the programme was classified as top secret, several details were revealed in advance of the selection of the winning design. At the time, it was confirmed that the bomber would be manned, but that unmanned operation was considered an option that could be implemented after the aircraft achieved initial operational capability (IOC) in 2025. Whereas it would initially carry conventional weapons, a nuclear capability would follow around two years after IOC.

Between 2011 and 2015, the USAF spent $1.9 billion on risk reduction efforts that allowed the two competitors to complete initial designs for the bomber.

Responses to the RFP resulted in the submission of two LRS-B designs from Northrop Grumman and a team comprising Boeing and Lockheed Martin. On October 27, 2015, Deborah Lee James announced plans to award an engineering and manufacturing development (EMD) contract to Northrop Grumman. The LRS-B project included a cost-reimbursable EMD phase that provided cost and performance incentives. Boeing protested the award with the Government Accountability Office (GAO) on November 6, 2015, and the USAF issued a 'Stop-Work' order to Northrop Grumman on the same day. Following its

review, the GAO issued its ruling, which denied the Boeing/Lockheed Martin protest and reaffirmed the USAF decision. The GAO's February 16, 2016, decision paved the way for Northrop Grumman to resume work on the new bomber.

The EMD phase was expected to cost around $21.4 billion in 2010, equating to $23.5 billion in 2016. Planned production included 100 bombers and based on that total, the average procurement unit cost (APUC) was required to be equal to or less than $550 million per aircraft in 2010 dollars or around $606 million in 2016 dollars. More recently, the USAF stated the APUC as $692 million in 2022 dollars.

Designation of the LRS-B as the B-21A was revealed in February 2016. Its designation was intended reflect its status as the USAF's 21st-Century bomber. In March that year, the USAF released a list of Northrop Grumman's partners and subcontractors on the programme. They included Pratt & Whitney, Janicki Industries, Collins Aerospace, GKN Aerospace, BAE Systems, Spirit Aerosystems and Orbital ATK.

On September 19, 2016, James announced that the bomber would be known as the B-21A Raider. The name was chosen to honour the 80 crew members under the command of American aviator Lieutenant Colonel James 'Jimmy' Doolittle that flew 16 North American B-25 bombers from the deck of the aircraft carrier USS *Hornet* (CV 8) and attacked targets in Tokyo and other locations in Japan on April 18, 1942. The bold mission by the so-called Doolittle Raiders took place just four months after Japanese forces carried out their surprise

An early morning view of the B-21A on the ramp at Northrop Grumman's facility in Palmdale, California. US Air Force

attack on Pearl Harbor, Hawaii, and was seen both as huge morale booster and one of turning points in World War Two.

Management of the B-21 programme is being led by the Department of the Air Force Rapid Capabilities Office (DAF RCO) under the direction of the Under Secretary of Defense for Acquisition and Sustainment. This lean approach differs from a typical development programme that is managed by larger offices using less agile processes and has resulted

in significant savings in both cost and time. Northrop Grumman also created a 'digital twin' of the B-21 that will facilitate and speed development of design changes in the digital world before they are applied to the aircraft.

Development of the B-21 was highly classified until the summer of 2015, when the USAF first unveiled details of the aircraft and the programme. Although it did not reveal technical specifications, the service did release the budget, acquisition strategy, procurement ▷

A tug prepares to pull a B-21A out of a shelter in preparation for testing at Edwards AFB, California. US Air Force /Giancarlo Casem

quantities and other aspects. In 2016, the USAF said the EMD effort would cost $21.4 billion in 2010 dollars, and, prior to the contract award, it spent nearly $2 billion on risk-reduction efforts. The weapon system's design was frozen following a critical design review that was completed in November 2018.

Until 2022, B-21 development was funded through USAF research and development (R&D) budgets. Procurement funds were first requested in 2022, when the USAF received $108 million for advanced procurement. The 2023 request for $1.78bn funded the first low-rate initial production (LRIP) lot of bombers. During these two years, the service received $2.87bn in research, development, test, and evaluation (RDT&E) funds and requested an additional $3.25bn. According to its 2023 budget request, the USAF expected to spend $19.1 billion in developing the B-21A. Northrop Grumman said it would absorb a $1.56 billion loss on the first five lots of B-21s, attributing this to inflation, higher-than-expected labour costs and supply chain issues.

Northrop Grumman is currently under contract to deliver six test aircraft assembled with the same tools, fixtures, processes, and systems used for the production models. Considered to be production-representative test vehicles (PRTV), they are being produced under the EMD phase of the long-range strike bomber contract. Although the six aircraft will initially support testing, they will be converted to operational configuration once developmental and operational checks have been completed.

The successful first flight of the bomber cleared the way for the USAF to issue the first LRIP contract to Northrop Grumman, which occurred in late-2023. The USAF plans for the initial B-21 acquisition to take place in five lots totalling 21 aircraft. The service will acquire the first 40 Raiders through fixed price contract options.

The bomber remains on track to meet its key performance parameter for APUC of $550 million in 2010 dollars, which equates to $792 million in 2024 dollars.

Testing and fielding

In March 2022, Northrop Grumman revealed that the first B-21A had been moved from the production facility to a calibration operation in Palmdale in preparation for ground testing. Loads calibration testing was completed in May. In October 2023, it was confirmed that the bomber had begun taxi tests in preparation for its first flight.

The B-21 will become the backbone of the bomber fleet according to former USAF Chief of Staff Gen Charles Q Brown Jr. The bomber will initially replace the B-1B and B-2A and operate alongside modernised B-52Js. However, it could eventually replace the BUFFs in the future. Those fleets currently comprise 45, 20 and 76 aircraft, respectively.

In 2019, the USAF announced the Raiders will initially be based at Dyess AFB in Texas, Ellsworth AFB in South Dakota, and Whiteman AFB in Missouri. Following the completion of an environmental impact report in 2021, Ellsworth was confirmed as the first B-21 main operating base (MOB) and the location of the formal training unit (FTU). On September 13, 2024, the AFGSC reported that the Secretary of the Air Force had approved plans that would make Whiteman AFB and Dyess AFB the second and third MOBs for the B-21A. The locations are currently home to B-2As and B-1Bs operated by the 509th and 7th Bomb Wings.

In September 2021, the Air Force Secretary Frank Kendall confirmed that five test aircraft were in production, and, at the time of the rollout, six developmental aircraft were under construction or test. The programme reduced risk by testing the bomber's avionics and subsystems in a surrogate aircraft.

Flight testing is being conducted at the Air Force Test Center at Edwards AFB, California, which hosts the B-21 Combined Test Force (CTF). In preparation for the B-21A's arrival at Edward, the 420th Flight Test Squadron (FLTS) was reactivated under the 412th Test Wing on October 4, 2019. ▶

The first B-21A departs the runway at Edwards AFB, California, at the start of a test flight. US Air Force /Giancarlo Casem

The B-21A conducts a test flight over southern California. Testing is being conducted by Northrop Grumman employees and USAF personnel. US Air Force

The B-21As first flight began at Air Force Plant 42 in Palmdale, California, and ended at nearby Edwards AFB. All testing has since been carried out by the 420th Flight Test Squadron and the B-21A Combined Test Force. US Air Force

The first B-21A returning to Edwards AFB at the conclusion of a test flight conducted by the 420th Flight Test Squadron. US Air Force/Juan Femath

Until inactivated on December 30, 1997, the squadron had been tasked with flight testing of the B-2A. As an integrated team, the CTF includes personnel from Northrop Grumman, the 420th FLTS and Detachment 5, Air Force Operational Test and Evaluation Center (AFOTEC).

Assets in Palmdale include a pair of ground-based airframes that are supporting structural integrity and fatigue testing that will confirm the aircraft's design service life.

In a May 2024 briefing, the USAF acquisition chief said that B-21A testing was "proceeding well" and that the bomber was working its way through test objectives.

Design

The B-21 was described by Tom Jones, president of Northrop Grumman's Aeronautics Systems, as "the world's first sixth-generation aircraft." He said the B-21A would allow the air force "to deter or defeat threats anywhere in the world."

Although its configuration is similar to the B-2A, the new stealth bomber features a wider, deeper fuselage and a taller, narrower cockpit area, with a revised windshield and window layout. A different long-span W-shape flying wing design results in a lower profile and nearly conformal tear-shaped engine inlets. Like the B-2A, the flying wing design distributes lift and weight across the entire span, providing a high lift-to-drag ratio, resulting in greater cruise efficiency.

The B-21's wingspan is estimated to be about 140ft, which is smaller than the B-2A's 172ft span. It has a length of about 55ft, compared to the 69ft B-2A. Both the engine inlets and exhausts are shielded from below and the exhausts are set back from the tail. The B-21 also has two symmetrically positioned triangular doors on its upper surface, which open to provide more air to the engines during ground operations, take-off, and landing. Dual wheel main landing gear indicate the B-21A probably weighs less than the Spirit, but its deeper fuselage likely contains larger weapons bays.

Eight computer-controlled surfaces located at the trailing edge of the wings and tail can be deflected to deliver the stability normally provided by a vertical stabiliser and fulfil the role normally taken by a rudder. Like the B-2A, the deflection is controlled by the aircraft's computer to keep the aircraft stable.

These features all contribute to the aircraft's stealth characteristics and its ability to penetrate enemy air defences. Defense Secretary Lloyd Austin said: "Fifty years of advances in low observable technology have gone into this aircraft, and even the most sophisticated air defence systems will struggle to detect a B-21 in the sky."

According to Northrop Grumman, the B-21A was developed with next-generation stealth

technology and advances in low-observable processes that will make the aircraft easier and less costly to maintain than earlier platforms. Additionally, the bomber has advanced networking capabilities and open systems architecture will enable rapid upgrades of new weapons and software.

Northrop Grumman used digital engineering tools, agile software development and advanced manufacturing techniques and materials to help mitigate production risks on the Raider. The bomber's digital design reduces the number of live-flight test points and will enable a shorter than usual test programme. As noted earlier, rather than a traditional prototype, the first Raider is a production-representative aircraft, which will shorten the time and costs usually experienced between testing and production.

Unlike earlier generation aircraft, the B-21 will not be updated through block programmes and was designed for rapid upgradeability, allowing it to quickly meet evolving threat environments. New technology, capabilities and weapons will be seamlessly incorporated through agile software updates and the open systems architecture provides built-in hardware flexibility. These features will ensure the Raider can continuously be updated to meet evolving threats and fulfil a critical role in the USAF's most complex missions. ∎

B-52H 60-0050 releases a test version of the Massive Ordnance Penetrator over White Sands Missile Range, New Mexico, on June 18, 2009. USAF

Arming the bombers

Air Force Global Strike Command's Rockwell/Boeing B-1B, Northrop Grumman B-2A and Boeing B-52H strategic bombers provide the US with the capability to rapidly project power precisely and globally. In addition to the capability to deliver a wide range of conventional weapons, the B-52H and B-2A bombers serve as one leg of the country's nuclear deterrent triad that also includes land-based intercontinental ballistic missiles (ICBMs) and submarine-launched ballistic missiles (SLBMs). Their range, payload and lethality guarantee the nation's ability to globally project airpower in support of national interests. The conventional and nuclear capabilities provided by the aircraft ensure that they can respond to any level of crisis as required by the National Command Authority (NCA).

Conventional gravity bombs

A variety of gravity bombs available to the AFGSC bombers include conventional unguided dumb bombs and precision-guided smart bombs. The standard low-drag general purpose (LDGP) bombs comprise the 500lb Mk 82s and BLU-111s, 1,000lb Mk 83s and BLU-110s, and 2,000lb Mk 84s and BLU-117s. When equipped with a joint direct attack munition (JDAM) guidance tail kit, the Mk 82/BLU-111, Mk 83/BLU-110, Mk 84/BLU-117 LDGP bombs and BLU-109 2,000lb high explosive concrete piercing (HECP) bunker busters are respectively known by the designations GBU-38, GBU-32 and GBU-31. The tail section contains an

inertial navigational system (INS), and a global positioning system (GPS) guidance control unit improves the weapon's accuracy by autonomously directing it to designated target co-ordinates.

Known as the laser JDAM, the 500lb GBU-54 is a flexible dual-mode weapon that can be used against both fixed and moving targets in all weather conditions. It combines the

JDAM's GPS/INS precision with laser-designated accuracy provided by the DSU-38 sensor. The weapon was first delivered in May 2008 and deployed in combat in Iraq three months later. Another version based on the 2,000lb MK 84 bomb is designated as the GBU-56.

The addition of a nose-mounted Paveway II laser guidance system and a fin kit to the Mk 82, Mk 83, and Mk 84 LDGP bombs allow the weapons to be guided to a designated target. A semi-active laser seeker and pneumatically controlled canards direct the weapon, while the air foil group (AFG) provides lift and stability. When equipped with the Paveway II kits, the weapons are assigned the designation GBU-12, GBU-16 and GBU-10. Installation of the Paveway III seeker on the Mk 84 and BLU-109 results in their designation as the GBU-24.

Developed specifically to attack the most hardened targets, the 4,000lb GBU-28 is also fitted with the Paveway III seeker. In addition to laser-guidance, the enhanced GBU-28 is equipped with inertial navigation and GPS guidance systems.

Airman assigned to the 5th Aircraft Maintenance Squadron transport a GPS-guided GBU-31 joint direct attack munition for loading onto a B-52H at Ellsworth AFB, South Dakota, on June 9, 2014.
USAF/SrA Anania Tekurio

A 5th Bomb Wing B-52H equipped with externally mounted AGM-86 air-launched cruise missiles on the flightline during US Strategic Command (USSTRATCOM) Exercise Global Thunder 19 at Minot AFB, North Dakota, November 1, 2018. *USAF/A1C Dillon J Audit*

non-nuclear bunker-buster ever produced. Flight testing was conducted between 2008 and 2010, after which the programme transitioned to USAF. The B-2A successfully test-dropped the GBU-57 for the first time in 2014 and four further drops were conducted over the US Army White Sands Missile Range in New Mexico in 2017. The weapon has been cleared for delivery by the B-2A, although it has also been delivered by the B-52H during testing.

The CBU-87, CBU-89 and CBU-97 are free-fall, unpowered, wide area cluster munitions, designed to achieve multiple kills against enemy armour, personnel, and support vehicles. Known as the combined effects munition (CEM), the 950lb CBU-87 is a cluster bomb that consists of an SUU-65/B tactical munitions dispenser (TMD) with 202 BLU-97 submunitions, or bomblets designed for use against armoured vehicles. The 700lb CBU-89 is a cluster bomb dispenser that deploys the GATOR system of air-dropped land mines. The SUU-64 TMD is equipped with 72 BLU-91 ▶

The enhanced GBU-49 Paveway II combines the laser-guidance of the GBU-12 with the GBU-38's GPS/INS unit. This permits the bomb to be employed either as a laser-guided munition with GPS/INS redundancy or as a GPS/INS-guided munition and provides the weapons with the accuracy of a laser-guided weapon, while retaining all-weather capability.

Also called the Increment II small diameter bomb, the GBU-53 Stormbreaker is a 250lb weapon equipped with a tri-mode seeker that features a millimetre wave (MMW) radar imaging infrared (IIR) and semi-active laser. It provides the capability to attack mobile targets from stand-off ranges through adverse weather.

Known as the massive ordnance penetrator (MOP), the GBU-57 is a GPS-guided, earth-penetrating weapon designed for use against hard and deeply buried targets. The MOP was developed in response to a USAF-led quick reaction capability (QRC) and tested through a partnership between the USAF and the Defense Threat Reduction Agency beginning in 2004 and is now managed by AFGSC. Weighing in at around 30,000lb, the Boeing-designed MOP is the most powerful and deeply burrowing

AGM-158 joint air-to-surface stand-off missiles are loaded on a 9th Expeditionary Bomb Squadron B-1B Lancer at Andersen Air Force Base, Guam. *USAF/A1C River Bruce*

Personnel from the 9th Expeditionary Bomb Squadron Aircraft Maintenance Unit prepare to load an AGM-158 joint air-to-surface stand-off missile into a B-1B at Andersen AFB, Guam, on May 9, 2020. *USAF/A1C River Bruce*

Airmen from the 2nd Aircraft Maintenance Squadron load GPS-guided GBU-31 joint direct attack munitions onto a B-52H during a Combat Hammer exercise at Barksdale AFB, Louisiana. USAF/A1C Jacob B Wrightsman

GPS-guided 2,000lb GBU-31 joint direct attack munitions await fitting on a 2nd Bomb Wing B-52H during Combat Hammer at Barksdale AFB, Louisiana, on March 10, 2021. USAF/A1C Jacob B Wrightsman

A weapons load crew from the 2nd Aircraft Maintenance Squadron load GBU-10 laser guided bombs onto a B-52H. USAF/A1C Jacob B Wrightsman

anti-vehicle (AV) and BLU-92 22 anti-personnel (AP) land mines. The CBU-97 sensor-fused weapon (SFW) also uses a SUU-64 TMD that contains ten BLU-108 tactical submunitions, each containing four hockey puck-shaped sensor-fused projectiles. Referred to as 'skeets', the infrared-guided projectiles are designed for use against armoured vehicles, artillery, and support vehicles. The SFW weighs around 915lb.

The wind-corrected munition dispenser (WCMD) is a tail kit that converts the CBU-87, CBU-39 and CBU-97 munitions into precision-guided bombs. When equipped with the tail kit the weapons are respectively known as the CBU-103, CBU-104 and CBU-105. The WCMD guidance kit incorporates an inertial navigation system (INS) and has flip-out control fins to steer the bomb. GPS data provided by the delivery aircraft is used to update the weapon's INS immediately before release. Following release, the WCMD's guidance corrects for launch errors and winds, and computes the optimum flight path and submunition release point. The kit gives the weapon a stand-off range of around 10 miles.

The B-52H can carry around 70,000lb of nuclear ordnance including precision and unguided bombs, mines, and missiles. USAF

Weapons personnel of the 5th Aircraft Maintenance Squadron load Mk62 500lb Naval QuickStrike mines into a B-52H during a Bomber Agile Combat Employment exercise. USAF/SrA Michael A Richmond

Weapon	B-1B	B-2A	B-52H
Conventional			
AGM-154 JSOW	x	x	x
AGM-158A JASSM	x	x	x
AGM-158B JASSM-ER	x	x	x
AGM-158C LRASM	x		
Mk82/84 LDGP Bombs	x	x	x
Mk62/65 QuickStrike Mines	x	x	x
CBU-87/89/97 Cluster Munitions	x	x	x
CBU-103/104/105 WCMD	x	x	x
GBU-31/32/38 JDAM	x	x	x
GBU-39 SDB 1	x		
GBU-54 L/JDAM	x	x	x
GBU-10/12/16/49 LGB	x	x	x
GBU-24 LGB	x	x	x
GBU-28 LGB		x	
GBU-53 SDB II	x		x
GBU-57 MOP		x	
Nuclear			
AGM-86B ALCM		x	x
B61-7/11/12		x	
B83-1		x	
AGM-181 LRSOM		x	x

A navigator from the 20th Bomb Squadron inspects 500lb Mk62 QuickStrike mines in a B-52H at Barksdale AFB, Louisiana, on August 1, 2022. USAF/SrA Jonathan E Ramos

Aerial mines

The QuickStrike is a family of shallow-water, aircraft-deployed mines used against surface and subsurface vessels. The QuickStrike mine is a standard general-purpose bomb fitted with a modular kit that includes an arming, detection and firing system. The Mk 62 and Mk 63 are converted general purpose 500lb and 1,000lb bombs. The Mark 65 is a 2,000lb mine that utilises a thin-walled mine case rather than a bomb body. The QuickStrike extended range (QS-ER) mine is fitted with a JDAM guidance kit. Equipped with acoustic, magnetic, and seismic sensors that permit them to detect passing ships and submarines, the QS ER can glide approximately 40nm from the launch aircraft when dropped from an altitude of 35,000ft. ▶

AGM-158 joint air-to-surface stand-off missiles are prepared for loading on a B-52H Stratofortress at Andersen AFB, Guam, on April 24, 2023. USAF/A1C Spencer Perkins

A B-52H from the 49th Test and Evaluation Squadron validated the ability to deploy inert JDAM QS-ERs from a stand-off distance of more than 40 miles at the Pacific Missile Range Facility off the coast of Kauai, Hawaii, in March 2023.

Conventional air-launched missiles

Th Raytheon AGM-154A joint stand-off weapon (JSOW) offers a stand-off range of 12-63nm and features GPS/INS guidance. The weapon carries 145 BLU-97 submunitions and is used to strike fixed and relocatable soft targets. The AGM-154C incorporates a 500lb blast/fragmentation/penetrator warhead effective against fixed-point industrial facilities, logistical systems and hardened tactical targets. It is equipped with long-wave imaging infrared seeker with autonomous target acquisition algorithms for precision.

Produced by the Lockheed Martin, the AGM-158A joint air-to-surface missile (JASSM) is an autonomous, precision cruise missile designed for use against heavily defended or high-value targets from stand-off ranges. The stealthy, low-cost weapon is equipped with GPS/INS guidance and imaging IR terminal seeker with a range of 200+ miles and can target fixed, relocatable, and moderately hardened/buried targets. The AGM-158B JASSM extended range (JASSM-ER) can hit targets at ranges of more than 500 miles. The weapon entered service in 2014 and was initially cleared for combat use on the B-1B in 2015. The newest version is assigned the designation AGM-158C and is known as the long-range anti-ship missile (LRASM). It achieved operational capability on the B-1B in 2019 and is also being cleared for carriage by the B-52H.

Nuclear weapons

Under the terms of the 2010 New Strategic Arms Reduction Treaty (START) with Russia, the US reduced the number of deployed nuclear weapon delivery vehicles to 700, including ICBMs, SLBMs and manned bombers (20 Northrop Grumman B-2As and 40 Boeing B-52Hs).

Tasked as a penetrating bomber, the Spirit is capable of delivering thermonuclear gravity bombs, but that mission is no longer assigned to the Stratofortress, which is no longer considered to be survivable in that role.

Air Force Nuclear Weapons Center (AFNWC)

Established on March 31, 2006, the Air Force Nuclear Weapons Center (AFNWC) is responsible for synchronising all aspects of nuclear materiel management on behalf of Air Force Materiel Command and in direct support of Air Force Global Strike Command. Headquartered at Kirtland AFB in New Mexico, its four major execution directorates comprise Air Delivered Capabilities, Intercontinental Ballistic Missile (ICBM) Systems, Nuclear Command, Control and Communications (NC3) Integration and Nuclear Technology and Integration. The AFNWC commander is dual-hatted as the Air Force Program Executive Officer (PEO) for both nuclear air-delivered and nuclear integration.

The Air Delivered Capabilities Directorate is responsible for delivering, sustaining, and supporting air-delivered nuclear weapon systems and oversees the Weapons Storage and Security System. It has operating locations at Eglin AFB in Florida, Joint Base San Antonio in Texas, Ramstein AB in Germany, Robins AFB in Georgia, Tinker AFB in Oklahoma, and Wright-Patterson AFB in Ohio. Programmes managed by the directorate include the B61-12 Life Extension Program and tail kit, Long Range Stand-Off Weapon, W80-4 warhead Life Extension Program. Additionally, it overseas the Weapon Storage and Security System, Secure Transportable Maintenance System, Protective Aircraft Shelter Interior Intrusion Detection System and Air-Launched Cruise Missile (AGM-86B) sustainment.

Responsibility for the integrated management of the LGM-30G Minuteman III and LGM-35A Sentinel ICBM systems is assigned to the ICBM Systems Directorate, which has operating locations at FE Warren AFB in Wyoming, Hanscom AFB in Massachusetts, Malmstrom AFB in Montana, Minot AFB in North Dakota, Vandenberg Space Force Base in California, and Washington DC. Its director is dual-hatted as the Air Force Program Executive Officer for ICBMs. Located both at Hanscom AFB and Kirtland AFB, the Nuclear Command, Control and Communications Integration Directorate is assigned the responsibility for deploying the AN/USQ-225NC3 weapon system across the USAF. The Nuclear Technology and Integration Directorate provides intelligence support to AFNWC and manages the nuclear certification process.

An inert QuickStrike extended range mine is attached to a B-52H operated by the 49th Test and Evaluation Squadron in March 2023. USAF

A B-52H assigned to the 49th Test and Evaluation Squadron conducting evaluations of an inert QuickStrike extended range mine at the Pacific Missile Range Facility off the coast of Hawaii. USAF

Carriage of the gravity weapons by the B-52H reportedly ended as early as 2010, but the B61-7 and B83-1 were not formally removed from the approved weapons configuration until September 2019. As a result of these changes, the B-52H is limited to carrying stand-off weapons.

Gravity bombs

The AFGSC's current inventory of around 475 gravity nuclear weapons includes the B83 and several variants of the B61. First fielded in 1968, the 715lb B61 thermonuclear bomb remains the primary nuclear munition in the US inventory. It has a variable yield of 0.3-360 kilotons (kT) and was produced in nine different versions. It can be delivered as a free-fall or retarded airburst, a freefall surface burst or in a 'laydown' mode from aircraft flying as low as 50ft.

First fielded in 1997, the bunker-busting B61-11 is a highly specialised deep-penetrating

A B-52H equipped with AGM-86 air-launched cruise missiles on the flightline during Exercise Prairie Vigilance 24-1 at Minot AFB, North Dakota, on October 23, 2023. USAF/A1C Luis Gomez

The 2nd Aircraft Maintenance Squadron prepares to load AGM-158 joint air-to-surface stand-off missiles on a B-52H during exercise Bayou Warrior on June 10, 2024. USAF/A1C Aaron Hill

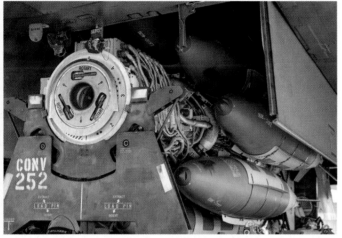
A launcher load frame equipped with eight inert GBU-31 joint direct attack munitions is raised into a B-1B at Dyess AFB, Texas, on January 9, 2023. USAF/SrA Josiah Brown

A B-52H assigned to the 69th Bomb Squadron equipped with 12 AGM-86B air-launched cruise missiles on its external pylons during Prairie Vigilance 24-3. USAF/A1C Kyle Wilson

version with a yield of 400kT. Development of the B61-12 life extension programme (LEP) began in November 2012.

The bomb's Boeing-developed tail kit assembly (TKA) contains a GPS-guidance system.

The B61-12 LEP can be air-delivered in either ballistic gravity or guided drop modes. The weapon utilises the 0.3-50kT warhead from the earlier B61-4.

On November 23, 2021, the B61-12 LEP achieved a major milestone when the Department of Energy's (DOE) National Nuclear Security Administration (NSSA) rolled out the first production unit at its Pantex plant in Amarillo, Texas.

In October 2023, the Department of Defense (DoD) announced plans to develop another modern variant, designated the B61-13. The weapon will feature the same TKA developed for the B61-12 and will replace the B61-7, which has a yield of 0.3-360kT.

Weighing 2,400lb, the B83 thermonuclear gravity bomb entered service in 1983 and has a yield of up to 1.2 megatons, making it currently the most powerful nuclear bomb in the US arsenal. Like the B61-11, the B83-1 is primarily intended to be used against deeply buried ▶

Airmen assigned to the 28th Aircraft Maintenance Squadron prepare to load 500lb Mk62 QuickStrike mines onto a B-1B during a Bomber Task Force mission. USAF/A1C/Audree Campbell

Nuclear Security Administration

Headquartered in Washington DC, the National Nuclear Security Administration (NNSA) is a semi-autonomous agency within the US Department of Energy. Established in 2000, it is responsible for enhancing national security through the military application of nuclear science: " NNSA maintains and enhances the safety, security, and effectiveness of America's nuclear weapons stockpile, works to reduce the global danger from weapons of mass destruction, provides the US Navy with safe and militarily effective nuclear propulsion and responds to nuclear and radiological emergencies both in the US and overseas.

NNSA's Pantex Plant, near Amarillo in Texas, is tasked with maintaining the safety, security, and effectiveness of the nation's nuclear weapons stockpile. Pantex supports nuclear weapons life extension programmes, nuclear weapons dismantlement, the development, testing and fabrication of high explosive components, and interim storage and surveillance of plutonium pits. It is the nation's primary site for the assembly and disassembly of nuclear weapons, carrying out final assembly of the upgraded B61-12 nuclear bomb.

The NNSA's Aerial Measuring System (AMS) is a component of the Nuclear Emergency Support Team (NEST) and is a rapidly deployable capability that can respond to all manner of nuclear incidents and accidents in the US and abroad. The AMS is comprised of several aircraft that provide real-time measurements of air and ground radiation contamination. Equipment on the aircraft includes state-of-the-art radiation detection and communications systems that ensure that airborne science teams can communicate in real time with experts at the national laboratories and support rapid protective action decisions. Scientists, technical personnel, and pilots are on-call 24/7, 365 days per year to deploy in response to nuclear incidents and accidents.

The five aircraft AMS fleet includes three fixed- and two rotary-wing aircraft that operate from Joint Base Andrews in Maryland and Nellis Air Force Base in Nevada. Three Beechcraft King Air 350 extended range fixed-wing aircraft were delivered in late 2019 and early 2020, replacing three King Air B200s that had been in service with the NNSA since the mid-1980s. In June 2024, a pair of Leonardo/AgustaWestland AW139s replaced two Bell 412 helicopters.

The aircraft are key components of the NEST, which is managed by the Office of Counterterrorism and Counterproliferation (CTCP) and includes NNSA's Radiological Assistance Program (RAP), Accident Response Group (ARG), Joint Technical Operations Team and National Search Task Force, National Atmospheric Release Advisory Center (NARAC) and the DOE component of the Federal Radiological Monitoring and Assessment Center (FRMAC). The aircraft support the AMS teams by conducting measurements of air and ground contamination following a nuclear or radiological accident or incident.

AMS frequently supports preventative nuclear and radiological detection operations in preparation of major National Security Special Events (NSSE), including political conventions, presidential inaugurations, the Super Bowl, Boston Marathon, and other major public events by conducting baseline surveys used to determine normal levels of radiation in the atmosphere. To support these public safety and national security missions, the King Airs are equipped with specialised equipment that includes a modular gamma-ray detection system and a high-resolution spectrometer to provide real-time measurements of low levels of air and ground contamination.

Two King Airs and one AW139 are assigned to the Remote Sensing Laboratory (RSL) at Joint Base Andrews. Another King Air and the second AW139 are stationed at the Nevada National Security Site's (NNSS) RSL at Nellis AFB.

Secure transportation

The NNSA's Office of Secure Transportation (OST) Program Office for Aviation Operations Division (AOD) operates two Boeing 737-400s and a single B737-700 from the Hangar 481 facility at Kirtland AFB in Albuquerque, New Mexico. The small OST fleet of passenger/cargo (combi) aircraft transport national security material and federal agents tasked with conducting secure ground transportation. Additionally, they support the DOE's emergency response capabilities. Although flown by NNSA crews, the aircraft are maintained by Yulista Solutions under the terms of a five-year $37.2m contract awarded in April 2024.

The NSSA's former airline-operated 737-400s were converted to combi configuration by Pemco World Air Services in 2011. The 737 combi configuration permits the aircraft to transport a combination of palletised freight in the forward cabin and 66 passengers in the rear, totalling approximately 40,000lb and has a range of more than 3,000 miles.

Additionally, the 737s were provided with an integrated cockpit avionics upgrade developed by Innovative Solutions & Support (IS&S). In addition to new digital instrumentation with flat panel displays, the upgrades provided the aircraft with enhanced flight management systems (FMS), a traffic collision avoidance system (TCAS), an enhanced ground proximity warning system (EGPWS), next-generation weather radar (NexRad), satellite communications (SATCOM) and automatic dependent surveillance broadcast (ADS-B) capabilities providing full communication, navigation, and surveillance/air traffic management (CNS/ATM).

A 737-700 that was converted to FlexCombi configuration by Pemco was delivered in October 2022. This can be configured to carry various loads of personnel and/or cargo. The FlexCombi offers three layouts that include up to 30,000lb of freight on six pallets with 24 passengers in the rear cabin or up to 35,000lb of freight on seven pallets with 12 passengers. When set up in full-freighter configuration, the aircraft can move up to 40,000lb of freight on eight pallets. One of the OST's 737s is always ready to support the agency's Nuclear Emergency Support Team (NEST) on a 24/7 basis.

and otherwise hardened high-value targets, such as strategic command and control bunkers and missile silos. The B-2A is certified to carry the B61-7, B61-11, B61-12 and B83-1.

Air-launched weapons

Full-scale development of the AGM-86B air-launched cruise missile (ALCM) began in January 1977 and Boeing had delivered 1,715 units when production ended in October 1986. Developed from the smaller AGM-86A, the 3,100lb missile is equipped with a variable yield of 5-150kT W80-1 thermonuclear warheads and uses a terrain contour-matching guidance system (TERCOM) to navigate to a preselected target. The ALCM first entered service with the B-52G-equipped 416th Bomb Wing at Griffiss AFB, New York, in December 1982. Since the retirement of the AGM-129 advanced cruise

AW139 N2314 arrives at Joint Base Andrews, Maryland, Maryland on June 17, 2024.
USAF/SrA Matthew-John Braman

One of two AW139s delivered to the US Department of Energy's National Nuclear Security Administration approaches St Mary's County Regional Airport, Maryland in 2024. Mike Wilson

missile (ACM) in 2012, the AGM-86B has been the USAF's only nuclear-capable cruise missile and around 530 remain in service.

The B-52H can carry as many as 20 ALCMs, with eight on the rotary launcher in its bomb bay and six under each wing. The weapon's wings, tail surfaces and engine inlet can fold for carriage and deploy upon launch. Powered by a Williams International F107-WR-100 turbofan engine, they have a range of more than 1,500 miles. Today, the weapon is only carried by the B-52H.

The ALCM will be replaced around 2030 by the AGM-181A long-range stand-off (LRSO) weapon. Development of the LRSO began in August 2017, when the USAF awarded Lockheed Martin and Raytheon $900m technology maturation and risk reduction (TMRR) contracts. Designed to penetrate and survive advanced integrated air defence systems (IADS), the new nuclear-armed, air launched cruise missile will be equipped with a 5-150kT

A B-2A operated by the 419th Flight Test Squadron drops a stick of 2,000lb general purpose bombs during tests near Edwards AFB, California, on March 5, 2003. USAF/Steven M. Zapka

A full load of eight AGM-86B air-launched cruise missiles on a B-52H rotary launcher assembly at Minot AFB, North Dakota, in 2014.
USAF/TSgt Aaron Allmon II

One of three King Air B300s operated in the nuclear safety role by the US Department of Energy's National Nuclear Security Administration Sunil Gupta

W80 Mod 4 (W80-4) thermonuclear warhead and will have a range of around 1,500 miles. It will be capable of operating in GPS-denied environments and delivering penetrating cruise missile capabilities through 2060. Raytheon Technologies was selected to develop the weapon system in April 2020, subsequently receiving an engineering and manufacturing development contract to develop the AGM-181 on July 1, 2021. The LRSO will be carried by the B-52H, B-2A and B-21A and procurement plans include 1,087 missiles. ∎

America's doomsday aircraft

595th Command & Control Group insignia

Known as 'Nightwatch', but more commonly referred to as the 'doomsday aircraft', the Boeing E-4B is a key component in the National Military Command System (NMCS). Officially known as the National Airborne Operations Center (NAOC) Weapons System, the highly specialised aircraft serves as an airborne command centre for the US President (POTUS), Secretary of Defense (SECDEF) and the Joint Chiefs of Staff (JCS). Its capabilities ensure continued critical command, control, and communication (C3) are maintained in the event of a national emergency or the destruction of ground centres. The aircraft provides "a highly survivable command, control and communications centre to direct US forces, execute emergency war orders, and co-ordinate actions by civil authorities."

In addition to the continuity of operations/continuity of government (COOP/COG) mission, the E-4B is tasked with the global command and control mission (GC2M) in support of the SECDEF during travel outside the continental US.

Since 1994, as part of the Defense Support of Civil Authorities (DCSA), the NAOC has also supported the Federal Emergency Management Agency (FEMA) by providing communications and command centre capability during relief efforts following natural disasters such as hurricanes and earthquakes.

Nightwatch

First known as the National Emergency Airborne Command Post (NEACP), the NAOC traces its history to February 1962, when Boeing delivered the first of three modified KC-135As to the USAF. On June 1, 1962, the 1000th Airborne Command and Control Squadron (ACCS) was activated under the 1001st Air Base Wing at Andrews AFB, Maryland, and assumed responsibility for the 'Nightwatch'. The aircraft stood alert at Andrews for the first time on July 1, 1962. Three Boeing EC-135Cs equipped for the Strategic Air Command's (SAC) 'Looking Glass' airborne command mission were modified for the NEACP mission by E-Systems under the designation EC-135J and entered service with the 1000th ACCS in 1966. The unit was redesignated as the 1st ACCS on July 1, 1969, and reassigned to the 1st Composite Wing at Andrews on July 1, 1976. The organisation later became the 1st Air Base Wing (ABW).

Advanced airborne command post

In February 1973, the Air Force Systems Command's Electronic Systems Division at Hanscom AFB, Massachusetts, awarded Boeing a $59 million contract to supply two 747-200B airframes, which would be modified as interim airborne command post aircraft under the Advanced Airborne Command Post (AABNCP) program (481B). The initial pair of aircraft had been ordered by a commercial customer but were never delivered. System integration

associated with the programme was carried out by E-Systems in Greenville, Texas. Although the E-4A carried the same basic systems as the EC-135J, it offered considerably more space and could remain airborne for longer periods. A third example was ordered in July 1973 and a fourth followed in December.

The initial E-4A flew on June 13, 1973, and was delivered to the 1st ACCS at Andrews AFB on December 23, 1974, with the second and third aircraft delivered on May 16 and September 15, 1975, respectively. The first E-4B flew on June 10, 1978, and was delivered to the USAF on January 7, 1980. It entered operational service later that month, standing the first NEACP alert at Andrews AFB, on May 22. On June 26, Boeing received a $418 million contract for the retrofit of the three E-4As to the later E-4B

One of four E-4B National Airborne Operations Center (NAOC) aircraft awaits it crew at Travis AFB, California, during a visit on September 11, 2017. USAF/Louis Briscese

configuration. They were returned to service in July 1983, May 1984, and January 1985.

Whereas the initial pair of aircraft was powered by Pratt & Whitney JT9D turbofans, the third and fourth had General Electric CF6 (F103) engines. The first two were later retrofitted with the GE engines.

Delivered in December 1979, the fourth aircraft featured distinctive faring on the back of the upper dec, that housed the antenna for the super high frequency (SHF) communication system. Assigned the designation E-4B, it also offered upgraded accommodation, additional shielding, and advanced electronics. It was also capable of being refuelled in flight.

The E-4B's communications suite includes very low frequency (VLF), low frequency (LF), medium frequency (MF), high frequency (HF), very high frequency (VHF), ultra-high frequency (UHF), super high frequency (SHF) and extremely high frequency (EHF) systems. A dual trailing wire antenna (DTWA) supports the operation of the

E-4B 73-1677 from the 595th Command & Control Group's 1st Airborne Command and Control Squadron prepares to receive fuel from a Wisconsin Air National Guard KC-135R Stratotanker. USAF/TSgt Codie Trimble

An E-4B departs Offutt AFB, Nebraska during the Defenders of Freedom Open House, and Air Show on August 30, 2009. USAF/Josh Plueger

Operations

Normally, the E-4B flight crew includes two pilots, a flight engineer and a navigator, however it is normally doubled for redundancy. The aircraft accommodate up to 94 crewmembers, including 30 battle staff and senior executives and officers. The aircraft retain analogue cockpits, which are viewed as being less susceptible to EMP than digital glass cockpits. A rest area and sleeping quarters for the flight crew is provided aft of the cockpit.

The E-4B main deck is divided into six functional areas that include a command work area, conference room, briefing room and operations team's work, communications, and rest areas. The lower deck houses the forward electronics bay, transmitters, and a maintenance workshop. Additionally, a retractable airstair permits easy access to the aircraft and reduces the need for additional ground support equipment. The aft section contains a trailing wire antenna (TWA) reel and operator station that enables VLF/LF communication with US Navy fleet ballistic missile submarines.

communications. Additionally, the E-4B can be equipped with an airborne launch control that makes it capable of remotely mounting retaliatory strikes. The E-4B conducted the successful launch of a Minuteman ICBM on April 1, 1980.

The 1st ACCS, which had been assigned to the Air Force Headquarters Command, was realigned under the Strategic Air Command (SAC), and transferred from the 1st Air Base Wing to the 55th Strategic Reconnaissance Wing (SRW) on November 1, 1975. Although the alert aircraft continued to operate from Andrews, the squadron was relocated to Offutt AFB on July 1, 1977. The 55th SRW was redesignated as the 55th Wing on September 1, 1991, and transferred to Air Combat Command (ACC) on June 1, 1992, following the deactivation of the SAC. The 1st ACCS was then reassigned to the 55th Operations Group (OG). Reflecting the addition of a support role for FEMA, the mission name was changed to NAOC in 1994.

Reporting directly to the Air Force Global Strike Command's Eighth Air Force at Barksdale AFB, Louisiana, the 595th Command and Control Group (CACG) at Offutt AFB, Nebraska, is currently responsible for the E-4Bs that remain assigned to the 1st ACCS. Maintaining the aircraft is the responsibility of the 595th Aircraft Maintenance Squadron. The 595th CCG was activated on October 1, 2016, and assumed responsibility for the 1st ACCS from the 55th OG the same day. The four-aircraft fleet is a part of the Nuclear Command, Control and Communications (NC3) network's aerial layer.

The USAF recently announced plans to activate the 95th Wing at Offutt AFB as part of a move to improve its strategic capabilities. Reporting to the 8th Air Force, the wing will assume control of the 595th CAOG, as well as several other units, and is expected to reach full operational capability in 2027.

Like many USAF aircraft, the E-4B is capable of being refuelled in flight, which greatly extends the duration of its mission. USAF/TSgt Codie Trimble

The 1st Airborne Command and Control Squadron operates four E-4B National Airborne Operations Center aircraft from Offutt AFB, Nebraska. USAF/SSgt Nicole Leidholm

The E-4B is based on the airframe of the Boeing 747-200 airliner but has been heavily modified to support its strategic communications mission. *USAF/Louis Briscese*

unrefuelled endurance of 12 hours. The aircraft provides seating for up to 111 people, including a joint-service operations team, USAF flight crew, maintenance and security component, communications team and selected augmentees.

An advanced satellite communications system permits senior leaders to remain in contact worldwide and the aircraft are provided with thermal effects shielding, acoustic control, an improved technical control facility and an upgraded air-conditioning system for cooling electrical components.

The 1st ACCS maintains at least one E-4B that is tasked as an NAOC and stands alert 24/7. It is staffed by aircrew, mission system operators and maintainers from the 595th CCG, along with highly specialised joint battle staff and an elite Raven security detail. Operations are directed by the Joint Chiefs of Staff (JCS) and executed through US Strategic Command (USSTRATCOM), which also provides personnel for the NAOC battle staff.

In addition to its national and NC3 mission, when required the E-4B supports FEMA, by providing communications and command centre capability to relief efforts following natural disasters, such as hurricanes and earthquakes. And whenever the President travels internationally aboard Air Force

Communications and data processing capabilities include extremely high frequency (EHF) military strategic, tactical and relay (MILSTAR) SATCOM, six-channel international maritime satellite and a tri-band radome that houses the SHF communications antenna. All four E-4Bs received Block 1 upgrades that enhanced electronic and communications infrastructure with commercial off-the-shelf (COTS) systems. Ongoing upgrades include replacing MILSTAR datalinks with advanced extremely high frequency system (AEHF)-compatible family of advanced beyond-line-of-sight terminals (FAB-T), replacing the VLF/LF transmitter with the low frequency transmit system (LFTS) and the legacy SHF with survivable super high frequency (SSHF), enabling uninterrupted, jam-resistant nuclear C2.

Powered by four 52,500lb st General Electric CF6-50E2 turbofans, the E-4B has a maximum gross take-off weight of 800,000lb and an

E-4B 73-1677 from the 595th Command & Control Group's 1st Airborne Command and Control Squadron conducts a training mission over the Midwest United States on May, 15, 2024. USAF/TSgt Codie Trimble

An E-4B assigned to the 595th Command & Control Group lifts off for a mission from its home base at Offutt AFB, Nebraska, on March 4, 2021. USAF/TSgt Codie Trimble

One, it is always accompanied by an E-4B on stand-by at an airport near the chief executive's location.

Recent communications upgrades to the E-4B installed the low frequency transmit system (LFTS) and advanced extremely high frequency Presidential national voice conferencing integration programme (APIP) modifications. The LFTS provides a single-wire low frequency communication capability and replaces the existing dual trailing wire antenna's very low frequency/low frequency (VLF/LF) transmit system, reducing aircraft weight by almost a tonne. The APIP transforms reliability and survivability of the E-4B SATCOM and national leadership command and control systems. Whereas Boeing and Collins Aerospace installed the LFTS modification, Raytheon

Based on the airframe of the Boeing 747-200 airliner, the USAF's E-4B is powered by four General Electric CF6-50E2 turbofan engines that each delivers 52,000lb of thrust. USAF

The 1st Airborne Command and Control Squadron regularly deploys its four E-4Bs to bases worldwide. One of the squadron's 'Nightwatch' aircraft visited RAF Mildenhall, England, on April 12, 2023. USAF/Karen Abeyasekere

Crew from the 412th Test Wing's 418th Flight Test Squadron, conduct aerial refuelling testing between a Boeing KC-46A and an E-4B Nightwatch. USAF/Christian Turner

Technologies installed the APIP modifications on the aircraft. In addition, L3Harris upgraded the aircraft's survivable super high frequency (SSHF) SATCOM system.

The advanced extremely high frequency (AEHF)-compatible terminal/Presidential national voice conferencing (PNVC) programme integrates AEHF-compatible command post terminals and PNVC capability onto the E-4B NAOC platform. These systems replaced the legacy military strategic, tactical and relay (MILSTAR) terminal, provide access to protected wideband AEHF satellite networks and replace the survivable emergency conferencing network (SECN).

SAOC

Plans for a replacement platform for the NAOC were first included as part of the USAF's FY 2018 budget, which requested funds to develop a new aircraft called the Survivable Airborne Operations Center (SAOC). At that time, the plans called for the SAOC to merge the missions of the E-4B and the US Navy's E-6B with a single aircraft. However, the navy decided to replace the Mercury with the E-XX platform based on the C-130J-30 Super Hercules. After several delays and changes to the scope of the project, it is now moving forward.

The Sierra Nevada Corporation (SNC) was selected to develop the SAOC weapons system that will replace the E-4B NAOC. The programme is part of broader efforts to modernise the Department of Defense's entire NC3 enterprise.

On April 26, 2024, the Air Force Life Cycle Management Center (AFLCMC) awarded SNC a $13.08 billion contract to develop and produce the SAOC. It initially obligated $59 million in research, development, test, and evaluation funds for work to begin. The contract covers the delivery of engineering and manufacturing development (EMD) and production aircraft, associated ground systems and interim contractor support.

An E-4B National Airborne Operations Center aircraft lifts off from Offutt AFB, Nebraska, at the start of a mission on July 10, 2019. USAF/SSgt Jacob Skovo

Operated by the 1st Airborne Command and Control Squadron, an E-4B National Airborne Operations Center aircraft aligns itself for take-off at Offutt AFB, Nebraska, 2015. *USAF Josh Plueger*

An E-4B drops away from the refuelling boom of a KC-135 from the 92nd Air Refueling Wing over Canada's Pacific coast, on April 10, 2014. *USAF/SrA Mary O'Dell*

The USAF had earlier eliminated Boeing from the competition citing issues over data rights and contractual terms.

Like the E-4B, the SAOC will be based on a modified 747. The commercial derivative aircraft will be "hardened to protect against nuclear and electromagnetic effects and modified with an aerial refuelling capability." It will be equipped with a modular open architecture system that will include secure C3 systems and a modern IT infrastructure. The service reportedly plans to acquire eight to 10 aircraft for the SAOC programme.

The USAF received $744 million for the SAOC programme in FY 2024 and requested $1.69 billion in FY 2025. It plans to spend $9 billion on the aircraft over the next five years., with work expected to be completed by July 2036. SNC is developing the next-generation SAOC with the assistance of a team of global aerospace and defence industry contractors that include RTX Collins Aerospace, FSI Defense, GE Aerospace, Greenpoint Technologies Inc, Lockheed Martin Skunk Works, and Rolls-Royce.

On May 8, 2024, Korean Air announced that it would sell five of its nine 747-8i airliners to Sierra Nevada. Valued at $674 million, the sale was aligned with Korean Air's plan to replace older aircraft with later generation platforms and is expected to close by September 2025. Sierra Nevada will convert the relatively young aircraft for the SAOC programme.

Although specific tail numbers were not disclosed, the first Korean Air Boeing 747-8B5, HL7630 (c/n 40905/1506), was delivered to Sierra Nevada's Aviation Innovation and Technology Center at Ohio's Dayton International Airport on June 4, 2024. It was registered to SNC as N747US on June 25, 2024. The SAOC programme is being managed by the Air Force Materiel Command's Program Executive Officer (PEO) for Presidential and Executive Airlift at Wright-Patterson AFB, Ohio. ∎

Known as the Survivable Airborne Operations Center (SAOC), the E-4B's replacement will be based on the Boeing 747-800 airframe. *SNC*

Mercury Rising

The Boeing E-6B is the largest aircraft in service with the US Navy. Originally designed to provide a communications link between National Command Authorities (NCA) and the service's fleet ballistic missile submarines, since October 1998 the E-6B has been tasked both as a communications relay platform and strategic airborne command post. Given the importance of its missions, the E-6B is aptly nicknamed after the Roman deity Mercury, the messenger of the gods.

In that role, it provides "survivable, endurable, and reliable airborne command, control, and communications (C3) between the US President, Secretary of Defense, and strategic and non-strategic forces, which include manned bombers, intercontinental ballistic missile (ICBM) silos and the Navy's fleet ballistic missile (FBM) submarines. It provides the capability to relay emergency action messages (EAMs) to all branches of the nuclear triad. As such, it provides US Strategic Command (USSTRATCOM) with the C3 capability required for the execution and direction of strategic-nuclear forces. It also serves as an alternate USSTRATCOM command centre, providing EAM origination and ICBM secondary launch capabilities. The platform is designated with the highest possible force activity designator (FAD) readiness level. Set by the Chief of Naval Operations (CNO), the E-6B requires 24/7 support, 365 days a year with a ready for tasking (RFT) that stipulates 12 aircraft be available at all times.

An E-6B operated by the US Navy's Air Test and Evaluation Squadron VX-20 performs a flutter test over Naval Air Station Patuxent River, Maryland, on August 3, 2016. US Navy/Erik Hildebrandt

It is the only survivable nuclear hardened weapon system aircraft capable of performing the chairman of the Joint Chiefs of Staff's critical nuclear deterrence through mobile C3 mission. The fleet typically flies 11,000 hours annually.

TACAMO

The Boeing 707-320B was selected as the winner of the US Navy's ECX programme in 1983 and assigned the designation E-6A.

The aircraft was developed to provide a communications link between the FBMs carrying submarine launched ballistic missiles (SLBMs) and NCA and was intended as a replacement for the Lockheed EC-130Q communications aircraft. Known as Take Charge and Move Out (TACAMO), the mission enabled communication with submerged submarines via airborne very low frequency (AVLF) communication systems.

A US Navy E-6B taxies after landing at Offutt AFB, Nebraska, on July 15, 2019. The Mercury is capable of launching US land based ICBMs.
USAF/SSgt Jacob Skovo

Strategic Communications Wing One insignia

Boeing received a $34 million contract to develop the new aircraft on April 29, 1983, and the first E-6A was rolled out at its Renton facility in Washington on December 18, 1986. It first flew on February 19, 1987, and arrived at Boeing Field in Seattle, where system integration was carried out. The initial aircraft was delivered to the US Navy for testing on July 22, 1988 and began replacing the EC-130Qs assigned to Fleet Air Reconnaissance Squadron VQ-3 on August 3, 1989, when the first two E-6As were delivered. Although initially nicknamed 'Hermes', the E-6A was renamed 'Mercury' in 1991. The fleet's transition from the EC-130Q to the E-6A was completed in June 1991.

The Mercury aircraft are flown operationally by Fleet Air Reconnaissance Squadrons VQ-3 'Ironmen' and VQ-4 'Shadows' from their main operating base at Tinker AFB, Oklahoma, and from deployed locations. Whereas VQ-3 maintains detachments at Travis AFB, California, and Offutt AFB, Nebraska, VQ-4 deploys its aircraft to Naval Air Station (NAS) Patuxent

River, Maryland. The E-6Bs also operate from other locations, as directed.

The E-6B fleet is supported by the TACAMO Weapons School and VQ-7 'Roughnecks' which is tasked as the fleet replacement squadron and is also based at Tinker AFB. The three squadrons and the TACAMO Weapons School report to the Commander Strategic Communications Wing One at Tinker. The operational fleet includes 15 E-6Bs and an additional aircraft that supports developmental efforts carried out by Air Test and Evaluation Squadron VX-20 at NAS Patuxent River.

Northrop Grumman is modifying an E-3D Sentry formerly operated by the RAF for use as a flight trainer by VQ-7. Purchased from the UK Ministry of Defence in June 2021 at a

cost of $15m, the TE-6B will fly around 600 hours annually and will reduce the stress on the operational E-6B fleet. Work to convert the aircraft into a trainer is expected to be completed during 2024. Once testing is completed at NAS Patuxent River, the TE-6B will be delivered to Tinker. Northrop Grumman supports the E-6B fleet under an $111m integrated maintenance and modification contract awarded in February 2022. Work associated with the contact, which runs through 2027, is carried out at the contractor's Aircraft Maintenance and Fabrication Center at the Chennault International Airpark in Lake Charles, Louisiana.

Powered by four 24,000lb st General Electric F108-CF-100 (CFM-56-2A-2) turbofan engines, ➤

Normally home-based at Tinker AFB, Oklahoma, an E-6B operates over Colorado while conducting refuelling operations with a KC-135R. USAF/Greg L Davis

Boeing delivered the first of 16 E-6As to the US Navy in 1988 and the Mercury fleet assumed the USAF's 'Looking Glass' command post role from 1998. USAF

the E-6A has a maximum gross take-off weight of 342,000lb and a range of 6,700nm with six hours of loiter time on station. With aerial refuelling and an augmented crew of 18, the Mercury could remain on station for up to 72 hours. The E-6A was normally operated by a crew of 12, comprising 2-3 pilots, a navigator and two flight engineers in the cockpit. Additionally, an aircraft commander (AC), airborne communications officers (ACO), airborne communications supervisor (ACS), two airborne communications operators (ACOMs), two in-flight technicians and a trailing wire antenna reel operator (RO) formed the mission crew. Its systems included AN/ALR-66 electronic support measures (ESM) and an AN/APS-133 weather radar.

The communications VLF equipment includes a 28,000ft long trailing wire antenna (LTWA) and a 5,000ft short trailing wire antenna (STWA).

Looking Glass

As the age of the USAF's EC-135C increased, the need for a replacement platform became apparent. Rather than procuring a new aircraft, the Mercury was selected to take on the 'Looking Glass' airborne command post (ABNCP)

Heavy maintenance on the E-6B fleet is carried out by Northrop Grumman at its Aircraft Maintenance and Fabrication Center in Lake Charles, Louisiana. Northrop Grumman

The US Navy's 16 E-6Bs are based on the Boeing 707-300 series airframe and are among the last examples of the airliner to be produced. USAF

Airmen from the USAF's 625th Strategic Operations Squadron conduct in-flight duties aboard a US Navy E-6B Mercury at Vandenberg Space Force Base, California, on October 31, 2023. USAF/SraA Joshua M Carroll

The US Navy operates 16 E-6B Mercury strategic communication aircraft including 15 that are assigned to Strategic Communications Wing One at Tinker AFB, Oklahoma. USAF

mission. The ABNCP modification programme began in February 1995, when Chrysler Technologies Airborne Systems (later Raytheon E-Systems) and L3Harris, received a contract from the US Naval Systems Command. The project transferred the Looking Glass ABNCP mission equipment from USAF Boeing EC-135s to the Mercury. The ABNCPs provided a back-up for USSTRATCOM's Global Operations Center (GOC) in the event that the underground facility at Offutt AFB, Nebraska, was unable to carry out its mission. The modifications added battle staff positions and other specialised equipment to the dual-mission aircraft, making it capable of fulfilling either the no-fail TACAMO or the Looking Glass mission.

Installed in place of the crew rest area, which was relocated to the back of the aircraft, the battle staff positions include the airborne emergency actions officer (AEAO), airborne operations officer (AOO), airborne launch control officer (ALCO), two command and control managers (CCMs), logistics planners and meteorological and oceanographic support officers.

In addition to the battle staff positions, the ABNCP mods installed an airborne launch ➤

An E-6B prepares to conduct an aerial refuelling evolution with a KC-135R from the Air Force Reserve Command's 507th Air Refueling Wing on August 23, 2019. USAF/Greg L Davis

automatic link establishment (HF-ALE) replacement and a commercial wideband satellite communication (SATCOM) capability.

Communications are being further improved through the incorporation of multi-role common datalinks (MR-TCDL) and the replacement of the E-6B's AN/ARC-208 military, strategic, tactical and relay (MILSTAR) SATCOM system with the advanced extremely high frequency (AEHF) family of beyond-line-of-sight terminals (FAB-T) and presidential national voice conferencing (PNVC) capability.

The first E-6B upgraded under the Block II programme was returned to the fleet on June 6, 2023. Carried out by Northrop Grumman at its facility in Lake Charles, Louisiana, the Block II upgrade included six modifications to improve the aircrafts' command, control and communications functions.

The E-6B's air refuelling capability extends the range of the important strategic communications platform tasked with maintaining secure links to the US land and sea-based ballistic missile forces. USAF/Greg L. Davis

control system (ALCS) that facilitates the activation of US land-based ICBMs in the redesignated E-6B. In addition to the capability to check ICBM status, the ALCS provided the E-6B crews with the ability to launch the missiles or change their target assignment.

Following these modifications, the Mercury became a command and control link between the NCA and US strategic forces, which include manned bombers, ICBM launch control centres (LCCs) and the Navy's SLBM submarines.

The Navy accepted the maiden E-6B aircraft in December 1997, and it flew its first mission in the new role on April 3, 1998. Full control of the dual operational mission was assumed by the E-6B on October 1, 1998. The Mercury fleet was completely updated to the E-6B configuration in November 2006, when the final aircraft was delivered.

A service life extension programme (SLEP) that began in 2009 and was completed in 2017

extended the E-6B service life from 27,000 hours to 45,000 hours and allows the aircraft to remain in service until 2038 or later. The multi-phase programme was carried out by the USAF's Oklahoma City Air Logistics Complex at Tinker AFB.

A Block I programme that replaced numerous obsolete components was carried out by L-3 Communications. The contractor delivered the first Block I E-6B in February 2009 and it achieved initial operational capability in 2014.

A multi-phase upgrade programme updated the E-6B's digital communication capabilities. It improved airborne command post operations and modernised direct over-the-horizon communications links with deployed strategic forces. In addition to the International Marine/Maritime Satellite (INMARSAT), the programme provided a high power transmit set (HPTS) technology upgrade, a high frequency

An E-6B at Vandenberg Air Force Base, California, on June 20, 2011, supporting the test launch of an unarmed operational Minuteman III ICBM. USAF/Jerry E Clemens Jr

A US Navy E-6B operating over the desert near Edwards AFB, California, on January 27, 2017. *USAF/Christopher Okula*

Battle staff

Located at Offutt AFB and reporting to the 595th Command and Control Group (CACG), the 625th Strategic Operations Squadron (STOS) is responsible for the team that operates the ABNCP systems aboard the E-6B. The squadron's ALCS Combat Operations Flight is tasked with several mission sets. Flying as integral members of the battle staff, the ALCS crew provides a survivable means to launch the US ICBM force. Additionally, the team provides intelligence, ad-hoc targeting, missile warning, battle damage assessment and ballistic missile defence support for the on-board airborne emergency actions officer (AEAO).

Twice each year, operational missile launch facilities and launch control centres are configured to simulate an unarmed ICBM launch using commands from an ALCS aboard an E-6B Mercury in a test known as a simulated electronic launch minuteman (SELM). The airborne system's reliability is also verified through the scheduled launch of an operational unarmed ICBM from Vandenburg AFB in California. Known as a 'Glory Trip', the test verifies the safety and reliability of the missile and launch systems aboard the E-6B.

The US Navy intends to retain the Mercury until around 2038 but will replace the E-6B with a specialised variant of the Lockheed Martin C-130J. The C-130G variant was first used in this role in 1963 and announced its intention to transition the TACAM Omission to the C-130J in December 2020. Transitioning the mission to the stretched -30 variant of the C-130J will bring the programme full circle. The new E-XX platform will only support the TACAMO mission, and the USAF plans to transition to the ABNCP mission and the ALCS to its planned fleet of seven survivable airborne operations centre (SAOC) aircraft.

The Navy plans to purchase the first three E-130J TACAMOs in 2027 and another six in 2028. The USAF has already begun acquiring the Boeing 747-800 aircraft to be modified for the SAOC role. ∎

The E-6A initially entered service with the US Navy in 1988 but assumed a joint services mission ten years later under the designation E-6B. USAF/Christopher Okula

Silos in the

In addition to being responsible for the USAF's entire fleet of manned bombers, the Air Force Global Strike Command (AFGSC) manages operations associated with the ICBM strategic weapon system. Assigned the designation LGM-30G and known as the Minuteman III, the ICBMs are a key element of the nation's strategic nuclear deterrent.

The LGM-30G is a three-stage, solid-fuelled missile and serves as the land-based leg of the US nuclear triad that includes the US Navy's UGM-133A Trident II submarine-launched ballistic missiles (SLBMs) and nuclear weapons carried by long-range B-52H and B-2A strategic bombers.

Dispersed in hardened silos to protect against attack and linked to underground launch control centres (LCCs), the missiles are dispersed across the American heartland in the northern tier states of Montana, North Dakota, Wyoming, Nebraska, and Colorado. Responsibility for the fields, which are spread over an area of 9,600 square miles is assigned to three missile wings, each comprising 133 missiles.

Personnel from the Air Force Materiel Command's 583rd Missile Maintenance Squadron prepare to install an LGM-30G Intercontinental Ballistic missile booster in a launch facility silo operated by the 341st Missile Wing at Malmstrom AFB, Montana. USAF/SSgt Delia Marchick

heartland

Minuteman

Development of the WS-133 weapon system was approved in February 1958 and Boeing's LGM-30A Minuteman IA was first deployed by the Strategic Air Command (SAC) at Malmstrom Air Force Base, Montana, in 1962. Malmstrom's 341st Strategic Missile Wing was the first of six Minuteman wings and its initial flight of ten missiles was placed on operational alert on October 22, 1962. Fielding of the LGM-30B Minuteman IB followed in 1963 at Ellsworth AFB in South Dakota, Minot AFB and Grand Forks AFB in North Dakota, Whiteman AFB in Missouri, and FE Warren AFB in Wyoming. Each wing included three or four 50-missile squadrons divided into ten-missile flights.

An LGM-30G Minuteman III ICBM blasts off from Vandenberg AFB, California, during a test launch on August 13, 2003. USAF

Replacement by the LGM-30F Minuteman II began in June 1965, with the final Minuteman Is withdrawn from service in 1969. On September 28, 1991, SAC was ordered to remove the entire fleet of 450 Minuteman IIs from alert status. Deactivation began in June 1992 and all of the missiles were retired by 1995. The last Minuteman II silo was destroyed at Whiteman AFB on December 15, 1997.

Development of the Minuteman III began in 1966, and the missile first entered service in June 1970. The Minuteman III has a maximum range of 7,020nm and is capable of carrying a payload of three re-entry vehicles (RV). The missile originally carried three 170kT W62 Mark 12 MIRVs, but later gained 300-350kT Mark 12A W78 RVs. Today, the missiles are equipped with a single more accurate 300- 475kT Mark 21 W87 RV. The missile is 59.7ft long, has a maximum diameter of 5.5ft and a launch weight of 79,432lb.

Boeing had delivered more than 800 missiles when production ended in November 1978. By 2008, the operational fleet had been reduced to 450 deployed missiles. Under the new Strategic Arms Reduction Treaty (START), the fleet was further reduced to just 400 missiles on June 2, 2017. However, 50 Minuteman III launch facilities are maintained in a 'warm' unarmed status that allows them to be reloaded should the need arise. All maintenance and security requirements continue to be carried out on the empty sites and each silo remains connected to the ICBM network. The first missile was removed in May 2015 from Minot AFB, but the empty launch facilities are equally spread between the three missile wings. ▶

20th Air Force insignia

Signed in 2010, the START agreement required the US to reduce its nuclear arsenal across the air force and navy to 700 deployed delivery vehicles. To meet this requirement, under the direction of the Office of the Secretary of Defense, the services reduced the number of strategic delivery vehicles to 400 deployed ICBMs, 60 deployed bombers and 240 deployed SLBMs.

The Minuteman III was the first US missile fitted with multiple independently targetable re-entry vehicles (MIRVs) and each ICBM was originally deployed with three warheads and 1,500 warheads were deployed on 500 launchers. In 2001, the US removed two warheads from 150 missiles in order to meet its START obligations. The drawdown began in 2012, when the three ICBM wings reduced the number of warheads fielded on each Minuteman to just one. The last MIRVs were removed in accordance with START II and New START agreements on June 16, 2014.

Although the Minuteman's replacement by the LGM-118A Peacekeeper ICBM began in December 1986, the last of 50 missiles that had been placed in service at Ellsworth AFB were retired in September 2005 under START II. The Peacekeeper was capable of delivering ten MIRVs with greater accuracy than any previous ballistic missile. ▶

Three Air Force Global Strike Command missile wings are responsible for 400 LGM-30G Minuteman III ICBMs installed in launch silos in five midwestern US states.
USAF/A1C Kristoffer Kaubisch

Each of Air Force Global Strike Command's three missile wings began receiving new transporter erector replacement programme (TERP) systems during 2023. *USAF/SrA Sarah Post*

On the truck:

U.S. AIR FORCE
21W00025
FOR OFFICIAL USE ONLY

OVERS

An LGM-30G is launched from a test site at Vandenberg AFB, California. Known as a 'Glory Trips', the operational test launches (OTL) of Minuteman missiles are carried out by the 576th Flight Test Squadron (FLTS) at Vandenberg. USAF

Artist's rendering of the LGM-35A Sentinel ICBM. *Northrop Grumman*

Based at Minot since June 1968, the 91st MW 'Roughriders' has been tasked with Minuteman III operations since April 1970, when the first missiles were accepted. Its 91st OG is responsible for the 740th MS 'Vulgar Vultures', 741st MS 'Gravel Haulers' and the 742nd MS 'Wolf Pack'.

The 341st SMW was activated at Malmstrom AFB on July 15, 1961, and assumed its current designation on July 1, 2008. Three operational units, comprising the 10th MS 'First Aces', 12th MS 'Red Dawgs' and 490th MS 'Farsiders', report to the 341st OG. The wing received its first Minuteman III missiles in January 1975.

The missile squadrons are comprised of five flights, with each assigned a missile alert facility that comprises ten unmanned LFs that are remotely controlled from a manned launch control centre (LCC). A two-officer crew is typically on duty in the LCC for 24 hours. The five flights are interconnected and status from any LF may be monitored by any of the five LCCs. However, control does not extend outside the squadron, meaning that only LCCs assigned to a specific squadron can control the LFs, which are located at least 3nm from each other and from any LCC.

A variety of communication systems provide the National Command Authority (NCA) with highly reliable links with each launch crew. In the event that command capability between

Recent modifications have provided the Minuteman with upgraded warhead fuses, networking, and cryptography systems. Upgrades to the guidance and propulsion systems and modernised re-entry vehicles were also applied. The Minuteman III has undergone multiple service life extensions throughout its history, making it the mainstay of US nuclear deterrence. Completed in 2015, the most recent was designed to keep the missile operational through 2030. Besides upgrades to the missile, the Launch Control Center Block Upgrade (LCCBU) replaced key hardware, software, communications, and environmental control systems in the crew capsule. Missile site security and video situational awareness upgrades were also carried out.

Operations

Assigned to AFGSC's 20th Air Force (20th AF) at FE Warren AFB, the current ICBM force includes 400 deployed Minuteman IIIs that are under the operational control of the 90th Missile Wing at FE Warren, 91st Missile Wing (MW) at Minot AFB and 341st Missile Wing at Malmstrom AFB. Each wing is responsible for three missile squadrons (MS), 133 missiles and 150 launch facilities (LFs) or silos.

Known as 'Mighty Ninety' the 90th Strategic MW was activated on July 1, 1963. Its 90th Operations Group (OG) is responsible for the 319th, 320th and 321st MS, which are respectively nicknamed the 'Screaming Eagles', 'Big Red' and 'Greentails'. The 90th MW has operated the Minuteman III since 1975 and has been assigned to AFGSC's 20th AF since December 2009.

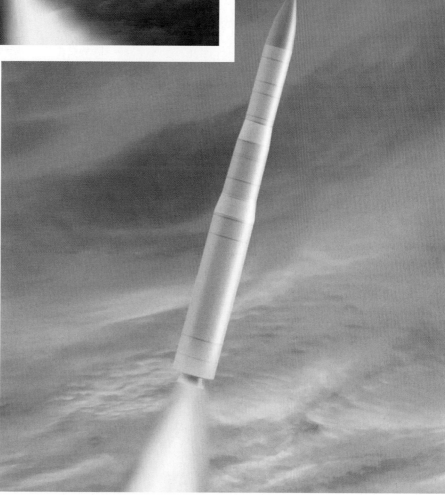

➤ **Artist's rendering of the LGM-35A Sentinel ICBM.** *Northrop Grumman*

A Minuteman III missile booster is lowered into the tube at Launch Facility-04 on February 25, 2015, during emplacement for Glory Trip-215. USAF

Inspecting an LGM-30G Minuteman III inside a silo about 60 miles from Grand Forks AFB, North Dakota, by a missile systems analyst with the 321st Organizational Missile Maintenance Squadron. USAF/Alan R Wycheck

the LCC and remote missile launch facilities is lost, the Airborne Launch Control System (ALCS) aboard the US Navy's E-6B aircraft automatically assumes command and control of the isolated missile or missiles. Airborne missile combat crews aboard the airborne LCC Mercury would execute the US President's orders.

Reporting to the USAF Weapons School at Nellis AFB, Nevada, the 315th Weapons Squadron (WPS) was activated in March 2012. It is tasked with delivering advance instruction in tactics and employment under the ICBM Weapons Instructor Course.

Maintenance

Originally designed with a 10-year service life, the Minuteman III has been operationally fielded for more than five decades. Support for the fleet is managed by the 309th Missile Maintenance Group, which is a component of the Ogden Air Logistics Complex at Hill AFB, Utah. The group's 583rd Missile Maintenance Squadron (MMXS) provides depot-level maintenance, and four geographically separated units provide on-site maintenance, repairs, and modifications of 450 Minuteman III launch facilities and 45 missile alert facilities and LCCs at Malmstrom, Minot and FE Warren, as well as Vandenberg Space Force Base (SFB) in California. It plans and directs repairs of ICBM

operational ground equipment, transportation and handling equipment, re-entry systems and unique support equipment. Additionally, it controls movement, provides storage for Minuteman III weapon system boosters, and performs static firing and depot-level maintenance for the Minuteman III. Each of the missiles undergoes programmed depot maintenance on an eight-year cycle.

Refurbishment of each missile requires around 22 days or about 600 hours. In addition, twice each year, one missile is removed from its silo and sent to Vandenberg Space Force Base (SFB) for a missile launch.

Testing

Reporting the 20th Air Force through the 377th Test and Evaluation Group (TEG), the 576th Flight Test Squadron (FLTS) is located at Vandenberg SFB, California, and is responsible for planning, preparing, conducting, and assessing all ICBM ground and flight tests. Activated at Vandenberg on September 1, 1991, it took on its current designation in July 1994 and has been assigned to the 377th TEG at Vandenberg since November 2, 2022. The 377th TEG reports to the 377th ABW at Kirtland AFB, New Mexico, as a geographically separated unit (GSU).

The 576th is responsible for conducting operational test launches (OTL) of Minuteman

missiles from the USAF's Vandenberg Test Range. Known as 'Glory Trips', the scheduled launches involve the removal of a randomly selected operational missile from a silo. After transporting the missile to Vandenberg, it is prepared for testing. The OTL is part of routine and periodic activities intended to demonstrate that the weapon system is safe, secure, reliable, and effective. Typically, three to four OTLs are conducted annually, with the most recent event occurring on November 5, 2024.

Unlike most launches, the Minuteman tested during Glory Trip GT 251 was equipped with three inert re-entry vehicles and was intended to confirm the weapon's ability to strike its targets with multiple warheads. The three test re-entry vehicles, which comprised one high-fidelity joint test assembly equipped with non-nuclear explosives and two telemetry joint test assembly objects struck targets some 4,200 miles down range at the US Army Space and Missile Defense Command's Ronald Reagan Ballistic Missile Defense Test Site on Kwajalein Atoll in the Marshall Islands in the central Pacific Ocean. During the flight, the radar, optical and telemetry data was collected in the terminal phase of the vehicle' flight to evaluate system performance. Like the GT 246 on April 2023, the back-up launch capability of the ALCS aboard a US Navy E-6B from Fleet Air Reconnaissance Squadron VQ-4 was validated when it was used to command the launch. Although each of the 400 fielded ICBMs is currently equipped with a single re-entry vehicle, the test launch verified the weapon system's ability to deploy three MIRVs. The Minuteman III launched in this test was removed from a silo at Minot AFB. Under the Hague Code of Conduct (HCOC) and a 1988 bilateral agreement, the US government formally notified 145 countries, including Russia and China, in advance of the launch.

Sentinel

Northrop Grumman is currently developing the next-generation nuclear ICBM that will replace Minuteman. The USAF Nuclear Weapons Center, ICBM Systems Directorate released a request for proposal for development and maintenance of a ground-based strategic deterrent (GBSD) on July 29, 2016. At the time, plans called for the new missile to be phased in over a decade, beginning in 2027, and was expected to have a more than 50-year life cycle. Boeing, Lockheed Martin, and Northrop Grumman all competed for the contract.

'Glory Trips' are part of routine and periodic checks to demonstrate that the weapon system is safe, secure, reliable, and effective. USAF

Boeing and Northrop Grumman were awarded three-year technology maturation and risk-reduction contracts by the USAF on August 21, 2017, respectively valued at $349m and $329m. However, Boeing withdrew from the project just days after the RFP was released and, on December 14, 2019, it was announced that Northrop Grumman would design and build the GBSD. On September 8, 2020, the contractor was awarded a $13.3 billion contract for engineering, manufacturing, and development (EMD). The new ICBM was formally designated the LGM-35A Sentinel in April 2022. Acquisition plans include 659 missiles, including 25 that will support developmental testing and the full deployment of 400 Sentinels. The programme is expected to cost around $141 billion.

Although the Sentinel will initially carry the same W87-0 nuclear warhead as the Minuteman III, it will eventually be equipped with the W87-1 that is under development. The new warhead will be installed in the Mk21A re-entry vehicle that is being developed by Lockheed Martin. In addition to the missiles themselves, the GBSD programme involves the modernisation of around 600 associated facilities spread across 40,000 square miles.

The first launch of an LGM-35A test missile is scheduled to occur in February 2026. Sentinel had been intended to reach initial operational capability by September 2030 but, in August 2024, the USAF announced that the programme would be delayed by at least three years due to cost overruns that necessitated restructuring the programme. Deployment of the Sentinel and retirement of the Minuteman III will be managed by the AFGSC's ICBM Modernization Directorate, which was activated at Barksdale AFB, Louisiana, in late 2023. ∎

Artist's rendering of the LGM-35A Sentinel ICBM. Northrop Grumman

144/25

SUBSCRIBE TODAY!

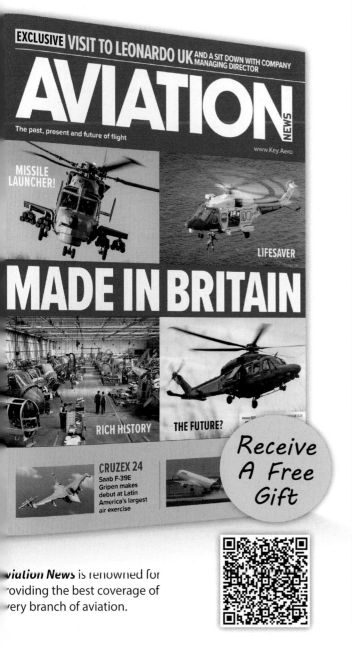

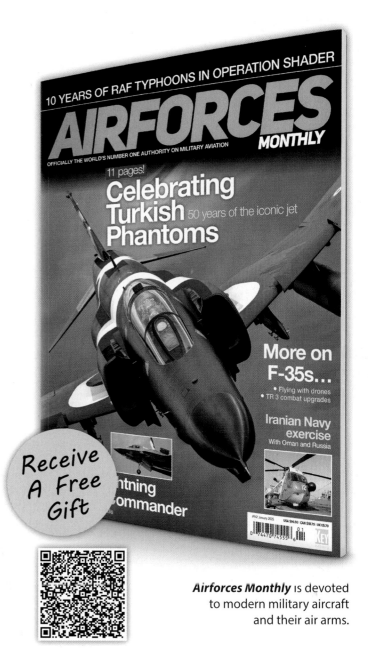

Aviation News is renowned for providing the best coverage of every branch of aviation.

Airforces Monthly is devoted to modern military aircraft and their air arms.

collections/subscriptions

Free 2nd class P&P on BFPO orders. Overseas charges apply.

Securing the Silos

582nd Helicopter Group insignia

The Air Force Global Strike Command (AFGSC) operates a small fleet of helicopters that support missions carried out across the northern tier of the United States, where the command maintains more than 450 Intercontinental Ballistic Missile (ICBM) launch facilities (LF). These silos are located in missile fields spread across five states: Colorado, Montana, Nebraska, North Dakota, and Wyoming.

Twin 'Huey'

The aerial support mission is currently fulfilled by Bell UH-1N Twin 'Hueys' that will soon be given a well-deserved retirement.

Based on Bell Helicopter's commercial model 212, the Twin 'Huey' first entered the USAF inventory under the designation UH-1N in 1970. More than 60 examples remain in service over five decades later. Unlike earlier single-engine versions of the 'Huey', the UH-1N is powered by the Pratt & Whitney Canada T400-CP-400 (PT6T-3/T400) Turbo Twin Pac. It combines a pair of PT6 turboshaft engines that are mounted side by side and drive a shared gearbox and single output shaft. UH-1Ns were initially fielded to the 20th Special Operations Squadron in 1971. Operating from Cam Ranh Bay Air Base in South Vietnam, the UH-1N primarily supported Special Forces missions.

Over a two-year period beginning in 1968, the service purchased 79 UH-1Ns that, in addition to combat support, were eventually assigned to varied roles including search and rescue, missile security, distinguished visitor, survival school and test support. Their eventual removal from the SAR role in the late 1980s allowed them to replace less capable single-engine UH-1Fs that were originally delivered to the Strategic Air Command (SAC) for missile wing support. The UH-1Fs were ordered in June 1963 as replacements for Sikorsky H-19s that had been used in that role.

The UH-1F was based on the US Army's UH-1B (Bell model 204) airframe but incorporated

A UH-1N from the 40th Helicopter Squadron manoeuvres in front of the US Strategic Command headquarters at Offutt AFB, Nebraska, on April 15, 2023. USAF/Katie Troyer

the UH-1D's (Bell model 205) 48ft main rotor, transmission, and longer tail boom. It also featured the General Electric T58-GE-3 turboshaft in place of the Lycoming T53. The USAF received 120 UH-1Fs and 26 TH-1Fs beginning in September 1963 and 20 were modified to UH-1P configuration for use by Special Forces.

Although still tasked to support SAC's strategic missile wings, the UH-1Ns were transferred to the Military Airlift Command and aligned under the Aerospace Rescue & Recovery Service's 37th Aerospace Rescue & Recovery Squadron (ARRS) in December 1973. Realigned under Air Combat Command in February 1993, the Twin 'Hueys' were placed under the control of Air Force Space Command (AFSPC) as part of the transfer of the ICBM force from Air Combat Command (ACC) on July 1, 1993. Since December 1, 2009, the missiles and helicopters have been the responsibility of AFGSC.

Today, the USAF's 63 UH-1N helicopters, which includes three acquired following their retirement by the US Marine Corps, serve with five different commands: Air Education Training Command (AETC), Air Force Materiel Command (AFMC), Pacific Air Forces (PACAF), the Air Force District of Washington (AFDW) and the Air Force Global Strike Command (AFGSC). The last two are the largest operators and are responsible for 19 and 25 helicopters, respectively.

AFGSC's UH-1Ns are currently operated by three squadrons assigned to the 582nd Helicopter Group (HG) at FE Warren AFB, Wyoming, as geographically separated units

TH-1F 66-1230 lifts off during the Strategic Air Command's Global Shield 79 exercise in July 1979. USAF

UH-1N 69-6601 operated by the 37th Helicopter Squadron ferries Secretary of Defense Chuck Hagel to a missile alert facility in western Nebraska during a visit to FE Warren AFB in 2013. USAF/RJ Oriez

(GSU). The 37th Helicopter Squadron (HS), 40th HS 'Pathfinders' and 54th HS 'Nomads of the North' are co-located alongside the 90th Missile Wing (MW) at FE Warren, 91st MW at Minot and the 341st MW at Malmstrom.

At one time assigned directly to the Operations Groups under the individual Missile Wings, the three squadrons have been aligned under the 20th Air Force Helicopter Operations Group (Provisional), which was established at FE Warren on August 1, 2014. The unit was designated as the 582nd HG on January 6, 2015. It was activated to improve mission effectiveness and standardisation within the three squadrons.

The helicopters are primarily tasked with nuclear security operations, which includes safeguarding each of the missile wing's Minutemen III ICBM LFs, airlift for the emergency security response (ESR) force, aerial surveillance and escort for ground convoys carrying nuclear munitions and serving as a communications relay. If required, they

can be tasked with aerial gunnery and close air support, as well as casualty evacuation assistance when participating in search and rescue missions.

In support of the emergency security response mission, the helicopters transport tactical response forces, are tasked with defending/protecting LFs and can conduct overhead surveillance and communications support for the teams. During nuclear convoy support missions, the UH-1Ns transport airborne response forces, provide communications support, and conduct overhead surveillance to ensure the security of the nuclear convoys. The UH-1N provides an integral link with the Missile Wing Security Forces Group's Tactical Response Force and are always present when weapon system components are transported to or from LFs.

Although the UH-1Ns can technically be flown as single-pilot aircraft, they are usually operated with a minimum crew of two pilots and a flight engineer/special mission aviator (SMA). ▶

UH-1N 69-6638 from the 37th Helicopter Squadron moves airmen from the 90th Security Forces Group during a training mission from FE Warren AFB on November 12, 2013. USAF/RJ Oriez

A UH-1N operated by the 54th Helicopter Squadron flies over Minot AFB, North Dakota, on May 11, 2021. USAF/Airman Allison Martin

version of the commercial AW139 produced by Leonardo's AgustaWestland subsidiary was selected over competing offerings from Lockheed Martin/Sikorsky Aircraft and the Sierra Nevada Corporation (SNC), which had both proposed variants of the Sikorsky UH-60.

Assembly of the basic AW139 is carried out at Leonardo's AgustaWestland facility in northeastern Philadelphia, Pennsylvania. After completing its initial flights, the rotorcraft are transferred to Boeing's nearby Ridley Park facility, where military-specific modifications and equipment is integrated. The initial $375m engineering, manufacturing, and development (EMD) contract covered integration of military-specific changes required to meet USAF requirements and delivery of four helicopters.

Commercial AW139s are in service with around 250 customers in 70 nations and the fleet has accumulated more than two million flight hours. Eight supplemental type certificates (STC) are included in the modifications required to convert the commercial AW139 aircraft to military configuration. Mods include the installation of special equipment in the baggage door compartment, external mounts for

A second flight engineer is normally on board for low-level routes and during night flights.

Headquarters AFGSC is designated as the lead command for the USAF's entire fleet of UH-1N helicopters, but Air Education and Training Command is responsible for the UH-1N formal training unit (FTU). Training for UH-1N crews is carried out at Kirtland AFB, New Mexico, by Detachment 2, 58th Operations Group, with six assigned Twin 'Hueys'. Activated on June 2, 2023, the unit assumed the mission from the 512th Rescue Squadron 'Flying Skulls'.

Since entering service, the helicopters have been equipped with upgrades that installed electro-optical infrared (EO/IR) sensors, crew-served weapons, night-vision compatible cockpits, terrain avoidance and warning, traffic collision avoidance systems, crashworthy aircrew seats and other modifications. However, the UH-1Ns no longer meet the command's speed, endurance, payload, or survivability requirements. As a result, AFGSC

moved forward with the acquisition of a follow-on system that will meet all nuclear security mission requirements and the Twin 'Hueys' will soon be replaced by the USAF's newest rotorcraft.

Grey Wolf

The USAF selected a Boeing-led team as the winner of its utility helicopter replacement programme on September 24, 2018, and awarded a contract with a potential value of $2.38 billion. Boeing had teamed with Leonardo to offer the latter's commercial AW139 helicopter to the USAF. The helicopter will "provide vertical lift support for nuclear weapon convoy escort, 24/7 adverse weather capable ICBM emergency security and operational support."

Plans originally called for the helicopters to replace Bell UH-1N Twin 'Hueys' used in the nuclear missile site security, training, test, and operational support airlift roles. The militarised

7.62mm M240 machine guns, a FLIR Systems Star SAFIRE 380-HDc electro-optical/infrared sensor and other systems. Additionally, a crashworthy, self-sealing fuel tank is installed and ballistic protection against small arms fire is added to the cockpit and cabin floor. Defensive aids include the AN/AAR-47 missile warning system (MWS), and AN/ALE-47 countermeasures dispenser set (CDS).

The USAF initially revealed plans to replace the Bell UH-1N fleet under its Common Vertical Lift Support Platform (CVLSP) programme on April 25, 2011. At the time the service expected to replace the entire fleet of 62 UH-1Ns with up to 93 new air vehicles via an incremental acquisition approach. Plans then called for the acquisition of two aircraft in 2012. CVLSP was expected to be an in-production, non-developmental, government off-the-shelf or commercial off-the-shelf (GOTS/COTS) aircraft.

The Aeronautical Systems Center (ASC) Capabilities Planning Division (ASC/XRX) at Wright-Patterson AFB, Ohio, issued a sources sought synopsis (SSS)/capability request for information (SSS/CRFI) to obtain market insight into potential solutions and sources ▶

Based at Malmstrom AFB, Montana, the 40th Helicopter Squadron is one of three units within the 582nd Helicopter Group that supports operations at three AFGSC bases. USAF

A UH-1N helicopter with the 40th Helicopter Squadron prepares to land during an integrated recapture and recovery exercise on June 11, 2019, at an ICBM launch facility near Simms, Montana. USAF/A1C Jacob M Thompson

A flight engineer guides a hoist onto a training target 50ft below a UH-1N from the 37th Helicopter Squadron during search and rescue training.
USAF/SSgt Christopher Ruano

An MH-139A lands on an open field at Eglin AFB, Florida, on April 5, 2024. The austere landing field test was conducted by the 96th Test Wing's 413th Flight Test Squadron. USAF/Samuel King Jr.

capable of providing at least 16 aircraft no later than September 30, 2017. Additionally, it cited the need for at least six of those aircraft to offer sufficient training and other support, including initial spares, support equipment, data, etc, in time to declare initial operational capability (IOC) no later than September 30, 2015.

Anticipated missions for the CVLSP included nuclear security operations/ICBM convoy support, emergency security response (ESR) via Tactical Response Force (TRF), National Capital Region (NCR) Operational Support Airlift (OSA),

aircrew system and tactics training, senior leader airlift (VIP), range support and survival, evasion, resistance, and escape (SERE) training. Although procurement was expected to begin in Fiscal 2012, the programme was cancelled in 2013 due to budgetary issues.

The USAF later considered issuing a sole-source deal for 41 Sikorsky UH-60Ms as replacements for the UH-1Ns, before moving forward with a "full and open" competition in 2017.

The USAF accepted its first MH-139A helicopter on December 19, 2019, when the initial example

arrived at Eglin AFB's Duke Field in Florida, wearing serial number 18-1002 and the civil registration N676SH. During a ceremony that commemorated its arrival, the rotorcraft was formally named the *Grey Wolf*. The name was chosen to pay homage to the canine species that are indigenous to the northern tier states where the largest number of the helicopters will be based.

The USAF added two system demonstration test article (SDTA) aircraft to its order on March 30, 2020. In accordance with the acquisition decision memorandum (ADM) dated March 3, 2019, the SDTA aircraft would be used to "expedite Type-1 training for operational aircrew, mitigate developmental test and evaluation (DT&E) schedule risk, and allow for concurrent fielding of operational capability while maintaining sufficient DT test assets to support any required follow-on testing".

The second MH-139A 18-1003 (c/n 41803) arrived at Duke Field on July 31, 2020, following a ferry flight from Pennsylvania. On November 9, 2020, AW139 (c/n 41237) arrived at Naval Air Weapons Station China Lake, California, for use as a live-fire test asset. A third helicopter was delivered to Duke Field on December 21, 2020, when 18-1001 (c/n 41801) arrived. Delivery of the flight test aircraft concluded in October 2023, when the second of the two SDTA aircraft was delivered to Eglin.

The initial helicopters were utilised by AFGSC Detachment 7, which was activated at Duke Field on December 18, 2019, to support testing and evaluation. Comprised of five pilots and six special mission aviators, the unit was aligned under the command's Strategic Plans Program & Requirements division. Detachment 7 worked closely with the Air Force Material Command's

413th Flight Test Squadron. Assigned to the 96th Test Wing, it is the USAF's only dedicated rotary wing test unit. On February 11, 2020, the MH-139A Combined Test Team (CTT) conducted its first flight with a mixed Boeing/USAF crew at Duke Field.

The USAF accepted the first four helicopters between August 9 and 19, 2022 after the Technical Airworthiness Authority (TAA) signed the development testing (DT) military flight release initiating the Air Force Military Utility test phase of DT. The milestones followed the Federal Aviation Administration's July 25, 2022, release of Supplemental Type Certification (STC) 2 for the MH-139A. On August 17, 2022, the 413th FLTS and AFGSC Det 7 conducted the first MH-139A flight under USAF ownership and operated solely by USAF personnel.

Flight testing was originally scheduled to run through late 2022, with a Milestone C decision permitting the MH-139A to enter low-rate initial production (LRIP) in September 2021. Delays resulting from the FAA tests of the required military modifications to the airframe caused the USAF to push back the LRIP plans from 2021 to 2022. The full rate production decision, which was originally expected in March 2023, was similarly pushed back. The acquisition decision memorandum (ADM) signed on March 3, 2023, authorised the first of three LRIP lots and, just days later, Boeing was awarded a $285m LRIP contract for 13 helicopters and training devices. A second LRIP batch of seven helicopters was ordered on April 19, 2024, when Boeing received a $178m contract. The second batch of helicopters will support the stand-up at FE Warren. LRIP is now expected to run through to 2025 and include 28 helicopters.–

The first LRIP helicopter flew in December 2023 and delivery of the initial production model to Malmstrom AFB occurred when serial 22-1009 arrived on July 31, 2024. Developmental testing was completed in February 2024. Under the current schedule, initial operational test, and evaluation (IOT&E) is scheduled to begin in late 2024 to support a full-rate production decision in 2025.

MH-139A 20-1006 prepares to land at Malmstrom AFB, Montana, on March 5, 2024. The Grey Wolf was the second of two System Demonstration Test Article (SDTA) models purchased by the USAF. USAF/SrA Breanna Christopher Volkmar

MH-139A 20-1006 taxies at Malmstrom AFB, Montana, after arriving from Eglin AFB, Florida, on March 5, 2024. USAF/SrA Breanna Christopher Volkmar

Fielding

The MH-139A is the first 'service-unique' helicopter acquired by the USAF and the first major acquisition in the ten-year history of the AFGSC. It is tasked as the lead command for the UH 1N Replacement programme. Fielding to the 550th Helicopter Squadron (HS) at Malmstrom AFB, Montana, began when serial 20-1006, the final SDTA aircraft, arrived on March 6, 2024. In November 2020, the Secretary of the Air Force announced the selection of Maxwell Air Force Base, Alabama, as the preferred location to host the MH-139A FTU under the Air Force Reserve Command's 908th Airlift Wing. The wing's 357th Airlift Squadron (AS) accepted its first MH-139A on April 3, 2024, and carried out its initial flight 21 days later. Ten helicopters are scheduled for delivery by the end of 2028. The former C-130H unit was redesignated the 908th Flying Training Wing (FTW) on July 20, 2024. On the same day, the 357th AS was inactivated and replaced by the newly activated 703rd HS. Operations at the schoolhouse are supported by Detachment 3, 58th Operations Group. Reporting to the 58th Special Operations Wing (SOW) at Kirtland AFB, New Mexico, as a geographically separated ▶

A flight crew from 550th Helicopter Squadron conducts an MH-139A training flight over the Highwood Mountains near Great Falls, Montana, on April 26, 2024. USAF/SrA Mary Bowers

unit, the detachment was activated on January 31, 2024.

Under the current schedule, the MH-139A will achieve IOC in February 2025, when seven mission aircraft are in service, and the required assets available (RAA) milestone is met. The first operational MH-139As will be assigned to the 582nd Helicopter Group's 40th Helicopter Squadron.

The utility helicopter replacement programme's 84 aircraft Acquisition Program Baseline (APB) was approved by the Air Force Acquisition Executive (AFAE) on September 11, 2018. However, the current Acquisition Program Baseline, which was approved on March 3, 2023, includes 80 MH-139As, comprising six development and 74 production aircraft. The total production quantity was re-phased and decreased from 78 to 74 due to the removal of PACAF requirements for four helicopters. The service will maintain a primary aerospace vehicle inventory (PAI) of 66 helicopters and plans to fly the MH-139A an average of 480 hours annually.

In March 2024, the USAF revealed plans that drastically scaled back MH-139A procurement, cutting acquisition from 80 to 42 aircraft, which essentially meant that the *Grey Wolf* would only replace the UH-1Ns assigned to the AFGSC. However, a subsequent change added back 14

Still wearing the civil test registration N676SH, an MH-139A lands at Duke Field, Florida, on December 19, 2019, before the helicopter's unveiling and naming ceremony. USAF/ Samuel King Jr

MH-139A procurement plans		
Lot	**No.**	**Notes**
EMD	4	
SDTA	2	
LRIP 1	13	FY22/23
LRIP 2	7	FY24
LRIP 3	8	FY25
FRP 1	2	FY26
FRP 2	4	FY27
FRP 3	7	FY28
FRP 4	9	FY 29
Total	**56**	

helicopters, resulting in a programme of record (POR) of 56 MH-139As.

In operational service, AFGSC's 33 MH-139As will be assigned to the 582nd Helicopter Group's three squadrons and each will receive 11 aircraft. AFGSC-specific mission training will be carried out at Malmstrom by the 550th HS, which was activated on May 25, 2023. The 550th HS 'Wolfpack' is serving as a provisional FTU for UH-1N units as they prepare for the transition to the MH-139A.It is also tasked with executing initial operational test and evaluation (IOT&E) for the *Grey Wolf*.

Fielding plans called for 25 *Grey Wolves* to be based at Joint Base Andrews, Maryland, with the 316th Wing's 1st HS for the AFDW's continuation of government/continuity of operations (COG/COOP) support mission. Additionally, the 36th Rescue Squadron, which supports the USAF Survival School at Fairchild AFB, Washington, will receive four. Due to the cuts in procurement, it remains unclear what the future is for those missions. The USAF had planned to purchase 74 production

aircraft between 2022-2030, including 28 in three LRIP lots. The SDTA helicopters will eventually be fielded to operational units, while the EMD aircraft will support ongoing testing of modifications and software with the 413th FLTS at Eglin. Planned for delivery to Malmstrom and Maxwell AFBs, the initial LRIP batch of 13 helicopters includes eight procured with 2022 funds and five with 2023 money.

The MH-139A is powered by two 1,531shp Pratt & Whitney Canada PT6C-67C turboshafts, has a maximum take-off weight of 15,432lb and a maximum payload of 5,600lb. It can carry nine fully loaded troops, has a 135kt cruise speed, a top speed of 167kt and can fly a minimum of four hours without refuelling while conducting the ICBM escort mission. If used for the COOP mission, it will deliver a minimum mission range of 225nm.

According to Boeing, the MH-139A cruises 50% faster, flies 50% farther, has 30% more cabin space and can lift 5,000lb more than the legacy UH-1N. It also has a modern digital cockpit

A Grey Wolf taxies after landing at Duke Field, Florida, at the conclusion of a test flight on February 22, 2024. USAF/SrA Breanna Christopher Volkmar

and a full autopilot capability that will reduce pilot workload.

Although the MH-139A was developed specifically for the USAF, the Italian Air Force operates a variant of the AW139M in the combat search and rescue (CSAR) role under the designation HH-139A. The rotorcraft previously saw service in the US when a pair of AB139s, as the aircraft was then known, began operations with the US Department of Homeland Security as long-distance, all weather, tactical apprehension aircraft in 2007. However, the AW139s were divested following their retirement in 2014 and passed on to a commercial operator in Canada.

The US Department of Energy's National Nuclear Security Administration operates a pair of AW139s that support the agency's Nuclear Emergency Support Team (NEST). The NNSA's newest aerial measuring system helicopters were delivered to the Remote Sensing Lab at Joint Base Andrews in Camp Springs, Maryland, in June 2024. The helicopters support the AMS teams by conducting measurements of air and ground contamination following a nuclear or radiological accident or incident. ∎

Grey Wolf developmental testing was carried out by the 96th Test Wing's 413th Flight Test Squadron at Eglin AFB's Duke Field in Florida. USAF/SrA Breanna Christopher Volkmar

Although built by Leonardo's AgustaWestland Philadelphia Corporation, system integration for the MH-139A was carried out by Boeing, which served as prime contractor for the programme. Boeing

Deploying the bombers

Beginning in March 2004, the USAF's Air Combat Command established a continuous bomber presence (CBP) in the US Pacific Command area of responsibility. Generally supported by individual expeditionary bomb squadrons (EBS) with six B-52Hs and more than 300 personnel, the rotational deployments typically lasted six months, alternating between the 2nd and 5th Bomb Wings at Barksdale Air Force Base (AFB) in Louisiana and Minot AFB in North Dakota, which took turns rotating to Andersen AFB in Guam every other year.

The CBP was a component of USAF's strategic deterrence mission and served as a visible reminder to allies, partners, and adversaries of US commitment to the region and its ability to respond to contingencies, if required. Although the mission was primarily supported by the B-52H fleet, B-2As also conducted rotational deployments to Guam. From February 2010, the Air Force Global Strike Command (AFGSC), assumed the responsibility for the deployments when it took control of ACC's B-52H and B-2A fleets.

A B-52H Stratofortress from the 20th Bomb Squadron rolls out after landing at Mihail Kogălniceanu Air Base, Romania on July 21, 2024. USAF/SrA Seth Watson

Pacific Base

Guam is the largest and southernmost of the Mariana Islands and is the largest island in Micronesia. It is the westernmost US territory in the Pacific and is more than 3,300nm west of Hawaii. Located on the northern end of the island, Andersen AFB – initially called North Field and later North Guam AFB – was established in 1944, following the liberation of the island from Japanese occupation. In 1949, the base was named for Brigadier General James Roy Andersen, who was killed in action on February 26, 1945, when his Consolidated C-87 was lost near Kwajalein in the Marshall Islands.

Andersen AFB supported the operation of Strategic Air Command B-52s from 1964 to 1990. It was an important base during the war in Southeast Asia from 1965 to 1972, when it hosted more than 150 B-52 bombers that carried out the Arc Light and Linebacker II missions. Between April 1970 and September 1990, B-52s assigned to the 43rd Strategic Wing – later the Bombardment Wing – were stationed at Andersen. Operations from the forward base considerably reduced the transit time required for the bombers to respond to situations compared to operating from their home stations in the central portion of the Continental US (CONUS).

In September 1996, two B-52Hs departed from Andersen and conducted a 34-hour, 16,000-mile round trip as part of Operation Desert Strike. During the mission, the bombers launched 13 AGM-86C conventional air-launched

cruise missiles (CALCMs) that struck power stations and communications facilities around Baghdad, Iraq.

The responsibility for operations at Andersen AFB is assigned to the USAF's 36th Wing, which serves as the host wing. It is part of the Pacific Air Forces (PACAF), the air component of the US Indo-Pacific Command (USINDOPACOM). Initially designated as the 36th Air Base Wing when it was assigned to Andersen in October 1994, the organisation assumed its current title in March 2006. The wing also supports operations of the 506th Expeditionary Air Refueling Squadron (EARS). The permanently assigned unit is comprised of multiple Air National Guard, Reserve and Active Duty KC-135 units that deploy for three-month rotations in support of the PACAF Tanker Task Force. In continuous use as a strategic platform for Indo-Pacific power projection for the US and partner nations since World War Two, Andersen has the largest fuel and munitions storage capacity in the USAF.

While acting as a forward-deployed deterrent force, the bomber crews were also provided with numerous training opportunities with allied forces during participation in joint exercises. Examples of the latter included the biennial Cope North and Valiant Shield, which were both hosted by the 36th Wing at Andersen.

An example of its use as a deterrent was demonstrated in early January 2016. In response to provocative claims by North Korea, a B-52H from Andersen was flown over Osan Air Base, South Korea. The low-level flyover was intended to demonstrate the US and South Korea's capability to respond to any threat at any time, according to the US Forces Korea commander.

Both the B-1B and B-2A also made deployments to Andersen in support of the CBP mission. The Spirit was first sent to Guam in February 2005, while the B-1B followed in September that year. Although the bombers often supported US Pacific

Escorted by a Finnish Air Force F/A-18C, a B-52H from the 2nd Bomb Wing refuels from a KC-135R from the 100th Air Refueling Wing during Bomber Task Force 24-4on July 21, 2024. USAF

Command (USPACOM) exercises in the area of responsibility (AOR), neither was permanently integrated into the CBP rotation. However, between August 2016 and February 2018, Lancers from the 34th, 9th and 37th EBS were assigned to the mission. B-52s, from the 2nd BW, had similarly replaced the 'Bones' in the US Central Command (USCENTCOM) AOR in April 2016. The deployment marked the return of the Stratofortress to that region for the first time in 25 years. The arrival of the B-1Bs followed their realignment under AFGSC, which occurred in October 2015. The July 2017 deployment of the 37th EBS to Andersen was the first for B-1Bs upgraded with Sustainment Block 16 modifications.

Bomber Task Force

Established to support the 2018 National Defense Strategy's Dynamic Force Employment concept, the Bomber Task Force (BTF) was a development of the US Strategic Command's earlier Bomber Assurance and Deterrence (BAAD) missions. Begun in 2012, the BAAD missions were led by US Strategic Command (USSTRATCOM) and were intended to demonstrate the credibility of the most flexible leg of the nuclear triad and provide essential training opportunities for personnel. The missions ranged in size from single to multiple sorties, exercises, and long-term power projection deployments. Both the BAAD and BTF missions demonstrate the ability of bomber force to provide a short-notice, flexible and vigilant long-range global strike capability. The BTF mission allowed the US Department of Defense to command and control bombers deployed anywhere in the world while increasing the agility of the force. ▶

A B-52H assigned to the 2nd Bomb Wing at Barksdale AFB, Louisiana, is secured after landing at Naval Support Facility, Diego Garcia, in support of a Bomber Task Force mission on March 22, 2024. USAF/MSgt Staci Kasischke

The first BTF deployment to Europe was conducted by the 23rd EBS, which flew four B-52Hs from Minot AFB to RAF Fairford in the UK in January 2018. The main aim of the deployment was to conduct theatre integration. The first BTF mission in the Pacific region was carried out by B-2As from the 509th BW's 393rd EBS, which deployed three bombers to Joint Base Pearl Harbor-Hickam, Hawaii, between August 15 and September 27, 2018. The concept was further developed in 2019 with the arrival of six 2nd BW B-52Hs at RAF Fairford in April 2019. The six aircraft deployment marked the largest to Europe since Operation Iraqi Freedom in 2003.

The USAF announced on April 16, 2020, that the 16-year CBP mission had been brought to a close. The final B-52H departure, which occurred the same day, followed the USAF's decision to cease basing strategic bombers outside the United States and transition to a 'dynamic force

employment' model that allows the bombers to operate from a broader array of overseas locations. The final CBP mission in support of the US Indo-Pacific Command was conducted by the 5th BW's 69th EBS, which arrived in July 2019. At the time, the AFGSC released a statement that read: "US strategic bombers will continue to operate in the Indo-Pacific, to include Guam, at the timing and tempo of our choosing. The dynamic deployments will be conducted by task force-size groups of bombers and will permit the US to be strategically predictable, and operationally unpredictable in sending the high-value assets to the Pacific."

Shortly after concluding the CBP mission at Andersen, the AFGSC revealed that it would maintain a deterrent by conducting regular rotations of small numbers of bombers to the Pacific and Middle East regions. These would not operate from bases such as al-Udeid Air Base in Qatar or Andersen for extended

periods. The move was intended to ensure the forces remained "strategically relevant and operationally unpredictable."

A similar deployment of six B-52Hs from the 2nd BW's 20th EBS concluded a four-month deployment to Diego Garcia in the Indian Ocean on March 31, 2020. The 20th EBS flew more than 90 sorties totalling 1,300 combat hours from the Indian Ocean base while assigned to the 379th Air Expeditionary Wing at Al-Udeid. The CENTCOM deployments had previously operated from Al Udeid but were relocated to Diego Garcia following Iranian rocket attacks on US bases in Iraq on January 7, 2020.

Less than one month after ending the CBP, four B-1Bs from the 7th BW's 9th EBS deployed to Guam from Dyess AFB, Texas. The bombers, which arrived at Andersen AFB on May 1, 2020, were deployed under the BTF dynamic force employment concept, developed to align with the National Defense

A pair of B-2A bombers conduct a training flight with EA-18G electronic attack aircraft from the Royal Australian Air Force's No.6 Squadron over the Pacific on August 19, 2024. The Spirits were deployed to Royal Australian Air Force Base Amberley, Australia in support of a Bomber Task Force mission. Australia, Department of Defence/FSGT Christopher Dickson

Strategy's objectives of strategic predictability and operational unpredictability. Although it no longer carries nuclear weapons, the B-1B offers a larger payload of conventional stand-off missiles and 2,000lb GBU-31 joint direct attack munitions than the B-52H. Additionally, the B-1 is capable of carrying the AGM-158C long-range air-to surface missile (LRASM), giving it an advanced stand-off, counter-ship capability. The Lancer's previous deployment to Andersen was conducted by the 9th EBS in 2017.

Prior to the arrival of Lancers at Andersen, B-1Bs performed multiple missions in the Indo-Pacific region. The first occurred on April 22 when bombers from the 28th BW at Ellsworth AFB, South Dakota, conducted bilateral and theatre familiarisation training near Misawa Air Base in Japan with USAF F-16Cs and Japanese Air Self Defence Force F-2As and F-15Cs. One week later, a pair of Ellsworth Lancers conducted a sortie over the South China Sea on April 29. Both missions were conducted as direct flights from Ellsworth.

A B-2A from the 509th Bomb Wing alongside a Royal Netherlands Air Force F-35A over the North Sea on March 18, 2020. The Spirit was operating in support of Bomber Task Force Europe 20-2.
USAF/MSgt Matthew Plew

Milestone deployments

Since establishing the BTF mission, AFGSC has conducted numerous deployments intended to demonstrate "the US commitment to collective security and to integrate with Geographic Combatant Command operations."

On May 5, 2020, two 28th BW B-1Bs conducted a long-range strategic BTF mission to the Baltic region. During the 25+ hour flight, the bombers carried out integration and interoperability training with Danish Air Force F-16AMs over the Baltic Sea and trained with Estonian joint terminal air controllers while delivering inert weapons at the Tapa Range. Before departing the region, the bombers conducted a low approach at Tallinn Airport, Estonia. The mission demonstrated the B-1B's long-range global strike capability, readiness, and the ability of the aircrews to integrate with foreign allies. Additionally, it enabled the aircrews to familiarise themselves with air bases, procedures, and operations in different Geographic Combatant Command areas of operation. The B-1B also integrated with Ukrainian Su-27s and MiG-29s for a ➤

Two B-1Bs from the 28th Bomb Wing are escorted by Ukrainian Air Force Su-27 and MiG-29 fighters on May 29, 2020. Ukrainian Air Force via USAF

Operating from Morón Air Base, Spain, while supporting a BTF Europe mission on May 31, 2021, a B-52H is escorted by a Belgian air force F-16A. Belgian Air Force via. USAF

long-range, long duration strategic bomber mission that carried them throughout Europe and the Black Sea region, on May 29. Prior to the deployment, B-1Bs had last operated in the European region in October 2018.

Six B-52Hs from the 2nd Bomber Wing deployed to Diego Garcia in January 2020 and conducted more than 90 operational bombing missions over Afghanistan, accumulating in excess of 1,300 hours of combat flight time. On August 11, 2020, three B-2As arrived at the British Indian Ocean Territory base, marking the first time since March 2016 that Spirits had been deployed to the facility.

Between August and September 2020, the 23rd EBS deployed six B-52Hs to RAF Fairford, where three B-52Hs carried out a sortie over Ukraine, operating alongside NATO allies and the Ukrainian Air Force. The mission preceded the Russian invasion of Ukraine that began in February 2022.

Four B-1Bs from the 7th BW's 9th EBS deployed to Norway's Ørland Main Air Station from February 21 to March 23, 2021. The deployment saw a B-1B land north of the Arctic Circle at Bodø Air Force Station in Norway on March 8, marking the first time a Lancer had operated from the base. Just four days later on March 12, a B-1B landed in Poland for the first time, conducting a mission from Powidz Air Base.

Four B-1Bs from the 28th Bomb Wing deployed to Diego Garcia for a bomber task force mission in October 2021, the first time Lancers had operated there in more than 15 years.

Three B-2As deployed to Keflavik Airport in Iceland for the first time on August 23, 2021. During the BTF deployment, which concluded on September 11, the bombers conducted theatre and flight training across Europe and Africa in conjunction with NATO allies and regional partners.

In March 2022, a B-2A visited RAAF Base Amberley, near Brisbane, Australia, for the first time. After making a direct flight from Whiteman AFB, a crew swap was conducted at the Australian base and integrated training was carried out with RAAF assets before the bomber returned home. Similar missions that began and ended at Whiteman were flown to Europe in December 2023. Supported by KC-135 and KC-10 tankers, four Spirits from the 393rd EBS later conducted a BTF mission to the base from July 10 to August 12, during which the bombers took part in the bilateral Exercise Koolendong 22 and conducted operations with RAAF F-35As, flying 34 sorties. The deployment was conducted as part of the Enhanced Air Cooperation (EAC), one of two Force Posture Initiatives (FPIs) established under the auspices of the US and Australian Force Posture Agreement to enable a rotational presence of the US aircraft in northern Australia.

Two B-52s assigned to the 5th BW's 23rd EBS landed at Kualanamu Airport, Indonesia, to participate in the Cope West bilateral interoperability exercise on June 19, 2023. Following the visit, which marked the first time B-52s had operated from Indonesia, the bombers returned to Andersen AFB to continue a BTF mission.

Three B-2As from the 393rd EBS were deployed to Keflavik Air Base in Iceland for a BTF Europe mission, arriving on August 13, 2023. Operating from Iceland during BTF 23-4, the bombers flew missions to Alaska and, on August 29, visited Norway for the first time when they refuelled at Ørland Air Station.

A B-52H operating from Andersen Air Force Base, Guam, conducts a low-level flight near Osan, South Korea, in response to provocative action by North Korea in 2016. USAF/SSgt Benjamin Sutton

B-1Bs assigned to the 9th EBS were deployed to RAF Fairford, UK, on October 12, 2023, for BTF-Europe 24-1. The bombers returned to Dyess on November 10.

B-1Bs from the 28th BW's 37th EBS conducted the first BTF mission to Luleå-Kallax Air Base, Sweden, on February 23, 2024. Although a pair of B-1Bs from the 7th BW landed at Luleå Kallax for the first time on June 19, 2023, the 28th BW deployment marked the first BTF mission to operate from the Swedish base. The aircraft and crews returned to Ellsworth AFB on February 29.

While European and Pacific BTF missions are often carried out from RAF Fairford and Andersen, 2024 has seen several milestones that included the first visits to airfields of allies. The 9th EBS from Dyess deployed four B-1Bs to Morón Air Base, Spain, for BTF 24-2 on March 24, 2024, which marked the first time the Lancer had deployed to the Spanish base. During the month-long deployment, the bomber crews conducted missions that provided training alongside the Czech Republic, Greece, Turkey, and the UK.

A B-52H from the 2nd Bomb Wing operates alongside Royal Australian Air Force F/A-18F Super over the Northern Territory for Exercise Talisman Sabre 23. Commonwealth of Australia, Department of Defence

A B-1B from the 28th Bomb Wing's 9th Expeditionary Bomb Squadron taxies at Dyess AFB, Texas, at the start of a US European Command Bomber Task Force deployment on October 11, 2023. USAF/SrA Sophia Robello

A B-1B from the 28th Bomb Wing's 37th Expeditionary Bomb Squadron arrives at Andersen AFB, Guam, on May 21, 2024, in support of a US Indo-Pacific Command Bomber Task Force mission. USAF/SSgt Jake Jacobsen

The trip concluded on April 23, when the bombers returned to Dyess.

A pair of B-52s from the 2nd Bomb Wing returned to Barksdale AFB, Louisiana, on April 3, 2024, after concluding a visit to Diego Garcia that began on March 22. Diego Garcia had supported B-52s that were engaged in combat operations over Afghanistan as recently as March 2020. During that deployment, crews from the 20th EBS flew more than 90 sorties and 1300 combat hours.

B-2As returned to Andersen AFB for the first time in five years on June 13, 2024. During the visit, the bombers participated in the biennial, multinational Exercise Valiant Shield around Guam, Palau, and the Northern Mariana Islands. B-1Bs from the 37th EBS that had been deployed to Andersen as part of BTF 24-6 also participated in the exercise.

Four B-52s assigned to the 5th BW's 69th EBS began flying missions in support of BTF 24-3 at RAF Fairford, England, on May 24, 2024.

Two B-52s from the 2nd BW arrived at Mihail Kogalniceanu Air Base, Romania, for Bomber

A pair of Swedish Air Force JAS-39 fighters escort a B-52H over Europe during a Bomber Task Force Europe 21-3 mission on June 09, 2021. USAF/TSgt Jael Laborn

Two Turkish Air Force F-16 Fighting Falcons fly alongside a B-52H Stratofortress, assigned to the 2nd Bomb Wing at Barksdale AFB, Louisiana, on May 26, 2021. USAF/TSgt. Jael Laborn

Escorted by Royal Australian Air Force F/A-18Fs and EA-18GS, a B-1B from the 28th Bomb Wing refuels from a KC-30A Multi-role Tanker Transport during Exercise Lightning Focus on December 8, 2017. The Lancers' participation in this exercise was part of the Enhanced Air Cooperation programme, which aims to increase the interoperability between the two allies. Australia, Department of Defence

Task Force 24-4, on July 21, 2024, marking the first time the bombers had operated from the Romanian air base. Prior to their arrival, the bombers were intercepted by two Russian Air Force MiGs over the Barents Sea. During the week-long deployment, the B-52s conducted operations with aircraft from Finland, Germany, the UK, Hungary, and Romania.

Three B-2As, comprising serials 82-1067 *Spirit of Arizona*, 82-1069 *Spirit of Indiana* and 93-1086 *Spirit of Kitty Hawk*, landed at RAAF Base Amberley on August 16, 2024. Crewed by personnel from both the 509th and 131st BWs, the arrival marked the first time since the summer of 2022 that Spirits had visited Australia. Supported by a pair KC-135Rs from the Illinois Air National Guard's 126th Air Refueling Wing, the Pacific bomber missions were focused on enhancing maritime strike capabilities in the region.

On September 24, 2024, the USAF announced it would continue bomber deployments to Australia as a strategic counterbalance to "China's growing assertiveness" in the region. In support of that plan, the US is investing in Australia's base infrastructure, including improvements at RAAF Base Tindal, Northern Territory, which will permit the joint civil/military facility to support up to six B-52s and refuelling aircraft in order to project power in the South China Sea.

More recently, in November 2024, the AFGSC deployed six B-52Hs to the Middle East marking the first time the bombers have been in the region since 2019. The deployment coincided with the departure of a USS *Abraham Lincoln* (CVN 72) carrier strike group from the region. The 5th BW bombers were deployed to Al Udeid Air Base, as part of the US response to attacks from Houthi rebels in Yemen and increased tensions following recent direct exchanges of fire between Israel and Iran as well as the former's ongoing operations against the Iranian-backed Hamas and Hezbollah terrorists in Gaza and Lebanon.

This deployment was another demonstration of the flexibility provided by the bomber fleet in response to world events. ∎

A B-2A from the 509th Bomb Wing's 393rd Expeditionary Bomb Squadron conducts aerial refuelling operations with a KC-135R assigned to the UK-based 100th Air Refueling Wing over the North Sea on September 16, 2019. USAF/TSgt Matthew Plew

Desert testers

California's Mojave Desert is home to Edwards AFB, which supports the USAF's largest and most important flight test organisation. Situated approximately 100 miles northeast of Los Angeles, the location is considered to be on the high-desert and Edwards is situated at an elevation of 2,300ft above sea level and spans 481 square miles. The base's 15,000ft concrete main runway is located adjacent to Rogers Dry Lake. When combined with a 9,000ft lakebed overrun, it provides one of the longest and safest runways anywhere in the world.

The military's use of the base's Rogers and Rosamond lakebeds can be traced to September 1933, when Army Air Corps aircraft from March Field in Riverside began conducting bombing and gun training on the Muroc Bombing and Gunnery Range. During World War Two, facilities were established adjacent to Rogers Dry Lake, then called Muroc Dry Lake, to train bomber and fighter crews for duty

(412th Test Wing Insignia)

overseas. It became Muroc Army Air Base in July 1942.

Its use as a flight test facility can be traced to October 1942, when the Bell XP-59A Airacomet, America's first jet-powered fighter, made its initial flight from Rogers Dry Lake. As the flight test programme progressed, it became evident that the lakebed coupled with year-round flying weather was ideal for all phases of aircraft testing.

In 1949, the Muroc Army Airfield was renamed Edwards AFB in honour of Captain Glen Edwards, co-pilot on the Northrop YB-49 jet-powered flying wing that crashed near the base on June 4, 1948. The Air Force Flight Test Center was activated at Edwards in 1951 and has been known as the Air Force Test Center (AFTC) since July 6, 2012.

A B-1B from the 412th Test Wing's 419th Flight Test Squadron performs a flight test with the Sniper advanced targeting pod on February 23, 2007. USAF/Steve Zapka

B-1B 85-0068 assigned to the 419th Flight Test Squadron at Edwards AFB, California, conducts a flyover during the Pacific Airshow in Huntington Beach on October 5, 2024. USAF/Richard Gonzales

Operated by the 419th Flight Test Squadron at Edwards AFB, B-1B 85-0068 lifts off for a mission testing the Sustainment Block 16A software upgrades on April 1, 2014. USAF/Ethan Wagner

Organisations

The 6510th Test Wing was activated on March 1, 1978, as a component of the Air Force Systems Command (AFSC) and assigned to the Air Force Flight Test Center (AFFTC) at Edwards. Both organisations were reassigned to the Air Force Materiel Command (AFMC) on July 1, 1992, and the wing assumed its current designation on October 2. The wing's history can be traced to the 412th Fighter Group (single engine), which had been activated at Muroc AAF on November 20, 1943, later operating from nearby Palmdale AAF, Bakersfield Municipal Airport, Santa Maria AAF and March Field, all in California. The group's duties included testing the P-59 and P-80 jet fighters.

Today, the 412th plans, conducts, analyses and reports on all flight and ground testing of aircraft, weapons systems, software, and components, as well as modelling and simulation work for the USAF.

Global Power-Bomber Combined Test Force

Known as the 'Silent Sting', the 419th Flight Test Squadron is tasked with developmental testing for the B-1, B-2 and B-52 bombers operated by Air Force Global Strike Command (AFGSC). It is also known as the Global Power-Bomber Combined Test Force.

The squadron has been associated with bombers since April 1942, when the 29th Reconnaissance Squadron was redesignated the 419th Bombardment Squadron (Heavy). Then assigned to the 301st Bombardment Group and operating the Boeing B-17F, it was among the first units to arrive in England as part of the US build-up of forces in August 1942.

B-52H 60-0050 from the 419th Flight Test Squadron takes off from Edwards AFB, California, while conducting a captive-carry flight test of the AGM-183A. USAF/Matt Williams

A B-52H assigned to the 412th Test Wing's 419th Flight Test Squadron operates over the Mojave Desert in southern California, on June 22, 2017. USAF/Christopher Okula

A B-1B taxies at Edwards AFB, California, November 20, 2020, at the start of a captive carry flight to demonstrate its external weapons capabilities. USAF/2nd Lt Christine Saunders

The unit's history was consolidated with that of the 6519th Test Squadron on October 1, 1992, and it was activated as the 419th Test Squadron (TESTS) the following day. Organised at Edwards in October 1989, the 6519th took over testing of the Boeing B-52G and B-52H Stratofortresses that had previously been carried out by the AFFTC's Strategic Systems Division. The squadron assumed responsibility for the Rockwell B-1 Lancer from the 6510th TESTS when that unit was inactivated in July 1991.

The 419th was aligned under the 412th TW's 412th Operations Group (OG) when it was activated on October 1, 1993, and it assumed its current designation on March 1, 1994. B-2A testing was first assigned to the 419th FLTS ➤

A KC-10A from the 22nd Air Mobility Wing at Travis AFB, California, transfers fuels to a B-52H flown by the 419th Flight Test Squadron over Southern California, on May 16, 2024.
USAF/Todd Schannuth

as operations engineers, test conductors or test directors, they co-ordinate the efforts of the flight test team, which includes aircrew, specialised engineers, maintenance personnel, programme managers, instrumentation technicians and range control officers.

In addition to full testing of new platforms, work typically includes ground and flight tests that conduct the initial investigation of the effects of engineering or design changes to an aerospace vehicle or its components, including envelope expansion weapons carriage and separation tests.

Recent tests carried out by the 419th FLTS have included evaluation of the AGM-183A air-launched rapid response weapon with the B-52H and the load adaptable modular (LAM) pylon installation on the B-1B.

Raider Testing

The 412th OG gained another squadron on October 4, 2019, when the 420th FLTS was reactivated to support testing of the Northrop Grumman B-21A. Although the Raider arrived

when the 420th FLTS was inactivated in December 1997.

The squadron primarily conducts developmental testing of new or upgraded aircraft systems, software, weapons, etc. However, it works closely with operational testers from Air Combat Command and the Air Force Operational Test and Evaluation Center at Edwards and alongside the operational bomb wings. Mixed aircrews often fly together on the same test missions, which supports more comprehensive evaluation of the system. Evaluations are also often supported by contractors that provide technical expertise for the system under test.

In addition to the traditional flight test crews that include pilots, navigators, weapons systems officers and flight test engineers, the 419th FLTS's Operations Engineering Flight is comprised of military, civil service, and contract engineers responsible for the overall planning of ground and flight test activities. Serving

The crew of a B-1B from the 412th Test Wing's 419th Flight Test Squadron prepares to conduct a captive carry flight with the AGM-158 joint air-to-surface stand-off missile. USAF/2nd Lt Christine Saunders

B-1B 85-0075 from the 419th Flight Test Squadron lifts off from Edwards AFB, California, for a flight test associated with the load adaptable modular pylon. USAF/James West

Named Spirit of Pennsylvania, B-2A 93-1087 is the latest Spirit to support test duties assigned to the 419th Flight Test Squadron. *USAF/Lindsey Iniguez*

B-2A 93-1087 Spirit of Pennsylvania *from the 419th Flight Test Squadron flies over Edwards AFB, California, on July 17, 2024.* USAF/Christian Turner

B-2A 93-1087 from the 419th Flight Test Squadron rolls out after landing at Edwards AFB, California, on July 17, 2024. *USAF/ Lindsey Iniguez*

Assigned to the 419th Flight Test Squadron, B-2A 93-1087 flies over the squadron's ramp at Edwards AFB, California, on July 17, 2024. One of the squadron's B-1Bs shares the ramp with both the assigned B-52Hs. *USAF/ Christian Turner*

at Edwards at the conclusion of its maiden flight on November 10, 2023, the USAF first acknowledged that flight testing at Edwards was underway in January 2024.

Testing of the sixth-generation stealth aircraft is being conducted by the B-21 Combined Test Force, which includes personnel from the USAF and Northrop Grumman. Operations are conducted by the 420th FLTS from facilities in the area of Edwards known as South Base.

Tenant Testers

Edwards is also home to Air Combat Command's 31st and 417th Test and Evaluation Squadrons, which are components of the USAF Warfare Center at Nellis AFB, Nevada. They report as geographically separated units of the 53rd Wing and its 753rd Test and Evaluation Group at Eglin AFB, Florida. When required, the 31st conducts initial operational test and evaluation (IOT&E) and utilises bombers assigned to the 419th FLTS at Edwards or loaned from operational squadrons. The 417th, which had previously conducted testing associated with the F-117A Nighthawk stealth fighter, was reactivated on April 24, 2018, to support OT&E of the B-21A. The squadron will become heavily engaged as the size of the Raider test fleet expands in the coming years. ∎

Humble, Approachable and Credible – the USAF Weapons School

Headquartered at Nellis Air Force Base (AFB), Nevada, the USAF Weapons School (USAFWS) trains tactical experts and leaders to control and exploit air, space and cyber on behalf of the joint force. Every six months, approximately 150 weapons officers and enlisted tacticians who are system experts, weapons instructors, advanced instructors, and leaders of air crews graduate from USAFWS. Although it reports to Air Combat Command (ACC) via the USAF Warfare Center (USAFWC), it provides training for personnel from several of the air force's major commands, including the Air Force Global Strike Command and the US Space Command.

Weapons officers and advanced instructors serve as advisors to military leaders at all levels, both those in uniform and in civilian government positions. Weapons school graduates train the USAF's instructors and the service's institutional reservoir of tactical and operational knowledge. Taking the mantra 'Humble, approachable and credible' as their creed, they form a band of trusted advisors and problem-solvers for the Department of the Air Force, enabling it to integrate its combat power seamlessly alongside those of other military services.

USAFWS graduates have played key roles in nearly every conflict and air campaign around the world for decades, at levels ranging from squadrons to campaign planners, strategists

and high-level leaders at air force and joint command levels. For Operation Desert Storm in 1991, the Strategic Weapons School – the Strategic Air Command's progenitor of what is now the 340th Weapons Squadron (WPS) – deployed virtually its entire faculty to fly combat sorties, serving as flight lead and commanders on dozens of missions. The USAFWS also provides academic and advisory support to numerous units, enhancing air combat training for thousands of personnel

from the USAF, Department of Defense and US allied services.

In addition, the USAFWS authors tactical doctrine and conducts tactics validation, actively collecting tactical knowledge and lessons learned from deployed units, evaluating solutions in exercises and formally preparing them for application across the armed forces. It provides a controlled learning environment and knowledge trust for best practices in land, air, space, and cyber combat techniques. The school also publishes the *Weapons Review*, the USAF's premier professional tactics publication.

Nellis-based and geographically separated Weapons Squadrons work very closely with the operational test and evaluation (OT&E) community. Test and Evaluation Squadrons supporting various systems are, in most cases, located on the same base as their respective Weapons Squadrons. For the bombers, the 49th Test and Evaluation Squadron (TES) at Barksdale AFB, Louisiana, works with the 340th WPS on B-52H issues, while the 337th TES at Dyess AFB, Texas, does the same with the 77th WPS on B-1B and the 72d TES at Whiteman AFB, Missouri, operates alongside the 325th WPS on the B-2A. Each of the bomber weapons squadrons trace their rich histories back to World War Two, when they were respectively activated as the 340th, 77th and 325th Bombardment Squadrons.

(US Air Force Weapons School Insignia)

Although marked as the flagship of the Air Force Reserve Command's 93rd Bomb Squadron, B-52H 61-0029 was flown by a crew from the 340th Weapons Squadron when it departed Nellis AFB, Nevada, for a Weapons School Integration (WSINT) exercise on June 2, 2021.
USAF/William R Lewis

(77th Weapons Squadron Insignia)

in Texas (B-1), 325th WPS at Whiteman AFB in Missouri (B-2), 340th WPS at Barksdale AFB in Louisiana (B-52) and the 509th WPS at Fairchild AFB in Washington (KC-135/Boom Operator).

Curriculum

USAFWS teaches graduate-level instructor courses that provide the world's most advanced training in weapons and tactics employment. During the course, which spans several months, students receive an average of 400 hours of academic instruction and participate in demanding combat training missions. The weapons instructor courses employ a 'building block' approach designed to produce weapons officers who become doctorate-level experts in a platform or specialty, as well as trailblazers in total force and joint integration planning and execution. ➤

USAFWS consists of 21 weapons squadrons and eight advanced instructor courses (AIC) at nine locations across the country. Thirteen squadrons are based at Nellis, including the 6th WPS (F-35A), 8th WPS (EC-130H/RC-135/E-3G/CRC/Weapons Director), 16th WPS (F-16), 17th WPS (F-15E), 19th WPS (Intelligence), 26th WPS (MQ-9/Sensor Operator), 32nd WPS (Cyber), 34th WPS (HH-60W/HC-130J/Special Missions Aviator), 57th WPS (Operational Support), 66th WPS (A-10/Joint Terminal Attack Controller), 315th WPS (ICBM), 328th WPS (Space) and 433rd WPS (F-22). The eight geographically separated units include the 14th WPS at Hurlburt Field in Florida (AC-130/MC-130/U-28/CV-22/Tactical Systems Operator/Special Missions Aviator), 29th WPS at Little Rock AFB in Arkansas (C-130J/Loadmaster) which also has the 29th WPS Detachment at Rosecrans ANGB, 57th WPS at Joint Base Lewis-McChord in Washington (C-17/Loadmaster), 77th WPS at Dyess AFB

A B-1B from the 28th Bomb Wing flown by a crew from the 77th Weapons Squadron departs Nellis AFB, Nevada at the start of a training mission during the US Air Force Weapons School mission employment exercise on December 7, 2011. USAF/SSgt Christopher Hubenthal

A B-1B flown by a crew from the 77th Weapons Squadron at Dyess AFB, Texas, takes off at Nellis Air Force Base, Nevada, during a US Air Force Weapons School Integration mission on November 22, 2022. USAF/SrA Zachary Rufus

The goal of the course is to train students to be tactical experts in their combat specialty, while also learning the art of battle-space dominance and integration of joint assets. This ability creates such a complete overmatch in combat power in any domain of conflict that adversaries have no choice but to submit or capitulate. Using an integrated approach means that USAFWS graduates are extensively familiar with their respective mission design series but are also trained in how all Department of the Air Force and Department of Defense assets can be employed in concert to achieve synergistic effects.

The culmination of the course is the Weapons School Integration Phase, conducted at Nellis AFB, in which all assets combine in challenging scenarios simulating current and future threat arenas. It involves a series of

(325th Weapons Squadron Insignia)

complex training scenarios carried out in a highly contested operational environment, requiring students to work together to plan and execute every aspect of air, space, and cyber combat operations. Students learn how to integrate air, space, and cyber capabilities in real-time to solve extremely difficult tactical problems. Additionally, they have to demonstrate their ability to lead and instruct while effectively integrating multiple weapons systems across the land, air, space, and cyber domains.

After graduation, the new weapons officers and advanced instructors return to the field to serve as unit weapons and tactics officers, leading combat missions and providing senior leaders and decision makers with tactical, operational, and strategic impact support.

The flagships of the 49th Test & Evaluation Squadron, 340th Weapons Squadron and 93rd Bomb Squadron supporting a Weapons School Integration exercise. USAF/William R Lewis

History

The roots of the USAFWS can be traced to 1949, when the Aircraft Gunnery School was established at Las Vegas Air Force Base, Nevada, which was renamed Nellis AFB in 1950. Although the Gunnery School converted to combat crew training to meet the operational needs of the Korean War, in January 1954 it assumed the mission of training fighter instructors. At that time, it was renamed the USAF Fighter Weapons School. Students at Nellis initially trained in North American F-51, Lockheed F-80, Republic F-84, and North American F-86 aircraft. By 1960, the North American F-100 and the Republic F-105 had become the two primary aircraft flown at the school.

In 1965, the Fighter Weapons School added the McDonnell Douglas F-4 to its fleet of aircraft. As the roles of fighter aircraft expanded during the Vietnam conflict, the vision and mission of the Fighter Weapons School was essential to the application of airpower. Many

(340th Weapons Squadron Insignia)

A B-52H from the 340th Weapons Squadron at Barksdale Air Force Base, Louisiana, on a US Air Force Weapons School Integration exercise at Nellis AFB, Nevada, on May 28, 2024. *USAF/William R Lewis*

of the air-to-ground and air-to-air innovations developed during the war in Southeast Asia can be attributed to its curriculum.

Assigned aircraft continued to change in concert with USAF inventories and technological advancements. The Weapons School deactivated the F-100 and F-105 courses but added the General Dynamics F-111 and LTV A-7D. Aggressor squadrons flying the Northrop T-38 and F-5 were established as part of the school in the early 1970s to improve air-to-air skills by providing accurate threat replication for dissimilar air combat training. The Corsair II's tenure in the school was a brief three years, as the squadron transitioned from A-7s to F-5 Aggressors in 1975. Continued modernisation saw the addition of the A-10A and the F-15A, which were integrated into operations in 1977.

A complete reorganisation in 1981 replaced the squadrons with divisions and saw the Aggressor squadrons transferred to the 57th Fighter Weapons Wing at Nellis. Additionally, the F-111 Division became a geographically separated detachment of the Weapons School. The newly formed F-16 Division graduated its first students in 1982. A 1984 expansion added a course to train weapons controllers in the F-15 Division. The end of an era occurred when the last F-4 class graduated in 1985, bringing an end to 20 years of Phantom weapons officer training. Later known as the Command and Control Operations (CCO) Division, the Air Weapons Controller Division was activated in 1987. The school A Fighter Intelligence Officers Course was added in 1988 and ➤

(315th Weapons Squadron Insignia)

became the Intelligence Division in 1990. The F-15E Division became part of the school in 1991.

Establishing the USAFWS

With the standing up of Air Combat Command in 1992, the school embarked on a dramatic shift from its 43-year focus exclusively on fighter aviation, dropping the 'fighter' from its title and assuming its current designation. The change was much more than symbolic, with the activation of the B-52 and B-1 Divisions that year. The two bomber divisions came over from the Strategic Weapons School (SWS), activated in 1989. The SWS graduated its first classes in 1990 and began developing the B-1B course in late 1991. Rescue helicopters joined the school

with the HH-60 Division in 1995, while the F-111 retired.

That year also saw the addition of RC-135 and EC-130 courses to the CCO Division. To increase the graduate-level understanding of space and air integration for operators, the school added the Space Division in 1996. With a growing need for weapons officers skilled at integrating all aspects of land, air, space, and cyber superiority, the USAFWS has continued to expand.

The year 2000 saw the addition of the E-8 Joint STARS to the CCO Division, as well as Special Operations Forces (SOF) instituting courses for the MH-53 and AC-130. Stealth technology joined the school in 2002 with the addition of the F-117 and B-2 Divisions. SOF added an MC-130 course that year as well.

In 2003, all of the USAFWS divisions were redesignated as squadrons and the Intelligence Sensor Weapons Instructor Course was added to provide graduate-level training in intelligence, surveillance, and reconnaissance integration. In 2006, the MH-53 and F-117 Weapons Instructor Courses were deactivated and the merger with the Mobility Weapons School added C-130, KC-135, and C-17 Weapons Instructor Courses. In 2008, the USAFWS added the F-22 and the MQ-1/9 Weapons Instructor Courses, with the ICBM Weapons Instructor Course under the 328th WPS arriving a year later. In 2012, ICBM was moved under the 315th WPS and the Cyber Warfare Weapons Instructor Course was added to complement the Space Course under the 328th WPS. Also in 2012, the Joint Terminal Attack Controller Advanced Instructor Course began, which officially became a Weapons

7

A B-1B departs Nellis AFB, Nevada, at the start of a Weapons School Integration mission on December 5, 2022. USAF/William R Lewis

B-2A 88-0331 **Spirit of South Carolina**
is refuelled at Whiteman AFB, Missouri,
June 6, 2024. USAF/MSgt John E Hillier

A pair of B-1Bs taxi for a Weapons School Integration (WSINT) mission at Nellis Air Force Base, Nevada,
May 30, 2023. USAF/William R Lewis

Instructor Course in 2015. Changes in 2017 included an HC-130J Weapons Instructor Course in the 34th WPS and the activation of the 6th WPS to conduct the F-35A Weapons Instructor Course. In 2018 the 32nd WPS was established, and the Cyber Warfare Weapons Instructor Course was aligned under it. In December of 2020, the Advanced Weapons Director Course officially became a Weapons Instructor Course under the 8th WPS, while the final F-15C class graduated in June 2021. In 2022, the 32nd WPS launched its Cyber Effects Operations Advanced Instructor Course.

Today, USAFWS encompasses 21 squadrons that deliver 31 weapons instructor courses, eight advanced enlisted courses and 39 combat specialties at nine locations. The 70+ year tradition of excellence associated with the USAFWS continues to adapt as today's USAF and Space Force graduates keep pace with the fast-moving world of military threats and technology and prepare for potential action against near-peer adversaries such as China or Russia. ∎